Best Bet Diet Cookbook

Recipes and strategies to help those affected
by Multiple Sclerosis achieve better health

Compiled by Joan Embry
Published by Direct-MS

To learn more about our charity for Multiple Sclerosis,
the Best Bet Diet and MS Hope visit:

www.direct-ms.org
www.mshope.com

Copyright © 2019 by Direct-MS

Published by Direct-MS
www.direct-ms.org
Registered Charity Number:
868267568RR0001

Illustrations: Brianna Schretlen
Photography: Krista Webb
Design: Kim Embry

ISBN: 978-1-9992610-0-9

Printed in Canada
Friesens Corporation
Altona, Manitoba, Canada

DEDICATION &
ACKNOWLEDGMENTS

This cookbook is dedicated to Roy Swank, Roger MacDougall and Judy Graham, the pioneers of the use of nutritional strategies for helping to keep Multiple Sclerosis well controlled. Their concepts and practical suggestions for nutritional changes to combat MS were published in the 1950s, 60s and 70s and are still valid today. This book is simply an extension of their monumental and selfless efforts to help persons with MS.

We would also like to dedicate this book to all the persons affected by MS and their families who have incorporated the Best Bet Diet into their lives and provided a great deal of feedback over the past 24 years. It has been inspiring and most gratifying to hear their success stories and their suggestions for improving the Best Bet Diet.

Above all, I have to offer my sincere thanks to my daughter-in-law, Kim Embry, who handled the design and layout of this book, took some of the photographs, and shepherded the book through the printing process. This cookbook would not have happened without her selfless, volunteer efforts and her unwavering attention to detail.

I would also like to thank my husband, Ashton Embry, for contributing the science section, my son, Duncan, for contributing numerous recipes and providing helpful suggestions for improvement, and my son, Matt, who inspired the need for the cookbook in the first place.

Thanks are also due to Krista Webb, who volunteered her time to take the many photographs in the book, to Brianna Schretlen who created the illustrations, to the individuals who shared their testimonials in the Living Proof section, and to the congenial staff at Friesens Printing who produced this book.

This book would have not been possible without the support of various groups of people. These include the enthusiastic cooks who provided their recipes, all the people who have generously contributed to Direct-MS and the Direct-MS Board which encouraged and financially-backed this project since its inception.

Finally, I would like to acknowledge Andrew Watson of Scotland who 20 years ago came up with the name Best Bet Diet for the proposed nutritional strategies for MS.

CONTENTS

Sailing to Better Health

When our son received the devastating diagnosis of Multiple Sclerosis in 1995, it felt like we had been thrown into the middle of a stormy sea. Having been a research scientist for 30 years, my husband Ashton plunged into the scientific literature for MS to determine the most likely factors which cause MS and to use this information to develop an effective therapy for our son.

In our research, we discovered abundant scientific evidence that indicates that various nutritional factors potentially play major roles in the onset and progression of MS. Strangely, this information was not being made available to persons with MS by doctors, nor by established MS charities.

Notably, many people are having great success in halting or greatly slowing MS with nutritional strategies; many testimonials are available. We are pleased to report that our son remains in excellent health. He has now started his own website, www.mshope.com, that explains the strategies he has used in order to stay healthy for the past 24 years.

My husband and I, with a group of others dealing with MS, decided to make this information freely available and established a federally registered charity which we called DIRECT-MS, short for **DI**et **RE**search into the **C**ause and **T**reatment of **M**ultiple **S**clerosis.

Our charity is dedicated to providing reliable, science-based information on the role that nutritional factors play in MS to allow those affected by MS to make an informed decision on whether or not to use nutritional strategies for managing the disease and preventing it from occurring in loved ones.

We hope you enjoy and benefit from the information and these recipes.

– Joan Embry

Introduction

About This Cookbook

This cook book has been prepared to help persons with Multiple Sclerosis implement the nutritional strategies which are recommended by our charity, Direct-MS and MS Hope. The following strategies are often referred to as the "Best Bet Diet" within the cookbook.

We would like to note that although we developed this diet as an effective strategy specifically to help people with MS, our research and some testimonials suggest it could be beneficial for persons with other autoimmune diseases, as well as anyone searching for better health.

We begin with a summary of the scientific concepts that link various nutritional factors to the MS disease process. To us, it is important to understand the basic scientific rationale for why various nutritional factors are a key part of the initiation and ongoing progression of MS. We then discuss the various foods which either contribute to the MS disease process and the foods which help to suppress and halt the disease process.

Clearly, it is essential to eliminate the pro-MS foods and to significantly increase the consumption of foods and supplements which counter MS. Thus, we have sections on foods to eliminate, foods to reduce, and foods to increase, as well as a list of supplements. We realize it is often very difficult to give up foods which you have enjoyed over a lifetime; such as dairy and gluten-containing products. To help you accomplish this, we discuss acceptable substitutes for common foods which are very problematic for MS. We have also provided suggestions for breakfast, lunch, dinner and snacks.

At the heart of this book are the recipes which we have gleaned from many sources and we ourselves have used over the past 24 years. We have ensured that each recipe follows the recommended nutritional strategies and that it can be prepared with relative ease.

We would also encourage you to develop your own recipes and adapt ones you discover by using the basic principles of the Best Bet Diet. The list of food substitutes should help ensure that any recipe does not contain foods to avoid.

We value your feedback on this book. Please feel free to send your comments to info@direct-ms.org

Scientific Concepts for the Best Bet Diet for MS

The Best Bet Diet is a nutritional strategy for managing MS that was developed by Dr. Ashton Embry in the 1990s. He formulated this diet after his son was diagnosed with MS by reading numerous scientific papers on multiple sclerosis and nutrition. A large volume of that research is available on our website www.direct-ms.org

MS is classified as an autoimmune disease. The basic disease process of an autoimmune disease, such as MS, is that a person's own immune system attacks specific parts of the body, which, for MS, is the central nervous system. The specific tissue that is the main target of the immune attack is myelin, a fatty substance that wraps around and insulates the nerve axons of the central nervous system. With the loss of myelin, the nerve axons themselves eventually are damaged and destroyed. The axons deliver instructions from the brain to all the parts of the body and their loss causes such messages to be delayed and blocked. This translates into the multiple disabilities that characterize MS.

Studies suggest that the MS disease process begins in childhood and that it is often 20–30 years before it becomes clinically apparent in young adulthood. Such a long lag time between the start of the disease process and its recognition characterizes many chronic diseases including cancer and heart disease.

It is now firmly established that genes play a significant role in the onset of MS and that only people who carry specific genes are susceptible to contracting MS. Studies have shown that many genes are involved in MS susceptibility with numerous genes related to the immune system being very important. It appears that less than 2 percent of people are genetically susceptible to MS.

Most importantly, it is also known that environmental factors also play a major role in MS onset and progression. Such environmental factors are those which result in one's own immune system attacking and destroying myelin in the central nervous system.

There are two main disease processes that result in myelin being attacked through autoimmune reactions. These are:

1. The activation myelin-sensitive immune cells by proteins from infectious agents and foods that closely resemble parts of one or more proteins in myelin. When the immune system defends the body against such foreign proteins, it also attacks the very similar looking proteins in myelin, a very unfortunate case of "mistaken identity".

2. The failure of the suppressor side of the immune system that usually shuts down any harmful autoimmune reactions such as an immune attack on myelin. An important part of the MS disease process is this failure to contain the autoimmune reactions caused by the immune reactions involving proteins from foods and infectious agents.

The Best Bet Diet has been formulated on the basis of identifying the foods that contribute to these two disease processes which drive MS and result in accumulating disabilities. Firstly, we will look at the various types of foods that contribute to the activation of myelin-attacking immune cells and this includes both the ingestion of harmful foods and deficiencies in beneficial foods.

Dairy products are very problematic for MS because they contain proteins that closely resemble myelin proteins. Myelin-attacking cells often become activated whenever the dairy proteins encounter the immune system. Lactose-free dairy products do not contain lactose, a sugar found in milk. Notably, it is the dairy proteins, not the lactose, which are part of the MS disease process. Such products should be excluded. Other foods that contain proteins that potentially can activate myelin-attacking immune cells are grains containing gluten and legumes.

Importantly, food proteins usually remain in the gut and are separated from the immune system by the gut wall which forms a barrier. However, some food proteins cause the gut wall to become leaky and to allow both food proteins and gut bacteria to pass through it. Proteins which are known to open up the gut barrier are found in gluten grains and in legumes.

Furthermore, the gut wall is also damaged by inflammation which often results from eating foods which cause allergenic reactions. Once the gut wall becomes open, food proteins and gut bacteria can pass through the barrier and encounter the immune system where they can activate myelin-attacking immune cells.

It is also important to note the existence of a second barrier which helps to protect the central nervous system from damage and prevent diseases such as MS. The blood vessels in the brain have much stronger walls than other blood vessels in the body. This barrier was designed to keep problematic immune cells and chemicals in the circulatory system out of the central nervous system, where they can do damage. This barrier is called the Blood Brain Barrier and it is well established that a damaged blood brain barrier is a characteristic feature of MS.

Just like the gut barrier, the blood-brain barrier is damaged and opened up by both proteins from gluten and legumes and by inflammatory reactions which are accompanied by oxidation. If myelin-attacking immune cells are present in circulation, they can access the central nervous system and myelin much more readily through a damaged blood-brain barrier.

Another factor which plays a major role in MS by way of gut health is the microbiome which consists of trillions of bacteria which live in the human gut. Recently, medical scientists have determined the importance of a healthy microbiome and how an unhealthy microbiome contributes to a variety of diseases including MS. The good gut bacteria promote well regulated immune reactions and strengthen the gut wall. On the other hand, refined sugar and artificial sweeteners, which are found in many food products, contribute to the occurrence of very unhealthy gut bacteria. Furthermore, a deficiency of fiber, also results in an unhealthy microbiome and the overgrowth of problematic bacteria. The bad bacteria are pro-inflammatory and increase gut leakiness and thus are part of the progression of MS.

Another substance that contributes to the activation of specific immune cells that attack myelin is sodium which is found mainly in salt. Clinical research confirmed this by demonstrating that MS patients with a high salt intake experienced 3 to 4 times higher rates of both relapses and new lesion development compared with MS patients with a low salt intake. The Best Bet Diet recommends a daily intake of sodium of no more than 1000 mg (1 gram) which approximates a Paleolithic intake This is much less than the average daily intake of sodium of Canadians which is about 3500 mg. Notably, about 70% of our sodium intake comes from packaged foods and restaurant meals. It is essential to read the sodium content on the nutrition label on all packaged products and to greatly reduce the consumption of foods with a high sodium content. Table salt can also supply a lot of sodium (1 tsp = 2350 mg of sodium). To offset this, one can use either "half-salt" or "no-salt" products which contain mainly potassium rather than sodium.

Now we can look at the nutrients which support the suppressor side of the immune system to ensure it functions well and keeps any autoimmune reactions well controlled. As discussed earlier, foods which promote a healthy microbiome contribute to better immune regulation. Other nutrients that increase immune regulation and help to control autoimmunity are:

Omega 3 polyunsaturated fat
Found in fish, game animals and a few plants such as flax.

Anti-oxidants
Include a range of vitamins, minerals and special substances found in fruits and vegetables.

Vitamin D
Comes mainly from the action of sunlight on skin and from some fish.

There is a large amount of scientific information that demonstrates these nutrients are very important for maintaining well-functioning, immune suppression. More importantly, there is also abundant information that links deficiencies of these nutrients to Multiple Sclerosis.

5 STRATEGIES TO PREVENT OR HALT MS

The Best Bet Diet or BBD was designed to accomplish five main tasks, all of which will potentially slow or halt the MS disease processes:

1. To greatly reduce the activation of myelin-sensitive immune cells by way of removing foods with proteins that closely resemble myelin proteins.

2. To promote immune regulation to control any sporadic autoimmune reactions by way of increasing foods and supplements that are known to accomplish this.

3. To greatly reduce or eliminate a Leaky Gut by removing foods that increase leakiness and adding foods and supplements which strengthen the gut wall.

4. To strengthen the blood-brain barrier with foods and supplements which ensure a strong barrier and eliminating foods which harm the barrier.

5. To ensure the presence of a healthy microbiome by eliminating foods which promote the growth of bad bacteria and by increasing high fiber foods and supplements that support the dominance of good bacteria.

BEST BET DIET BASICS

Based on the five strategies to prevent or halt MS, the basics of the Best Bet Diet are to eliminate, reduce and increase certain foods. Please see the Meal Strategies Section on pages 36–50 for a more detailed list of what foods to avoid and food substitute options.

ELIMINATE

Foods that contain proteins which have the potential to cause autoimmune reactions and/or increase intestinal permeability. These are:

- All dairy products (e.g. milk, lactose free products, cheese, yogurt).

- Foods containing gluten grains (e.g. wheat, rye or barley).

- Legumes (e.g. beans, soy, peanuts. peas, green beans and lentils).

- Any food that causes an allergic reaction as determined by a body reaction or a blood test.

- Candy, soft drinks and foods with a high sugar content as well as foods with artificial sweeteners. These foods alter the gut flora which in turn can cause a leaky gut and problematic immune reactions.

REDUCE

- Foods that contain saturated fat. Eat lean cuts of red meat (beef, lamb, pork) only a couple times a week.

- The intake of omega 6 polyunsaturated fats which are found in margarine, salad oils, and many baked goods. Use extra virgin olive oil (monounsaturated fat) for fat supply.

- Non-gluten grains such as corn and oats. Use mainly rice for grain products and eat these in moderation as a high consumption can adversely affect the gut flora.

- Alcohol consumption. At best, drink wine and spirits in moderation and completely avoid beer.

INCREASE

- An abundant intake of a wide variety of fruits and vegetables for plentiful fibre and antioxidants.

- Eat skinless chicken breast, game meat and fish for protein content. Fish such as salmon and mackerel also contain omega 3 polyunsaturated fat, which is very beneficial.

- Increase the use of extra-virgin olive oil for cooking and baking.

- Take a variety of supplements to bolster immune regulation, to strengthen the gut barrier and blood brain barrier, to increase anti-oxidant capacity, to promote a healthy microbiome, and to avoid deficiencies.

Increase

Lean Proteins

- fish
- chicken

Fruits & Vegetables

- a wide variety of fruits and vegetables rich in fibre and antioxidants

Supplements

- vitamin D3
- omega 3
- calcium
- magnesium
- vitamin B
- probiotics

Nuts & Seeds

- almonds, cashews, walnuts, pecans, pumpkin seeds, sunflower seeds

Reduce

Non-gluten grains   Alcohol

Omega 6
polyunsaturated fats

Saturated fats

Gluten grains

Legumes

Dairy Products

High sugar content
& artificial sweeteners

Eliminate

PROTECTION FROM MULTIPLE SCLEROSIS

Multiple Sclerosis is an autoimmune disease which can result in serious disabilities. Because genetics play a significant role in MS, close relatives of persons with MS are at high risk of contracting MS.

It is worthwhile for them to use a few simple nutritional strategies to greater lower and likely eliminate their risk of MS.

Two nutritional factors that are implicated in MS by abundant data are deficiencies in vitamin D and fish oil. Data from areas where MS rates vary from low to high indicate that a high supply of vitamin D either from sun exposure or the consumption of fish will greatly lower the risk of MS.

Persons at high risk of MS should ensure they have a high intake of vitamin D and fish oil. For children ten years old and younger, a daily supplement of 1000 IU of vitamin D and 2 grams of omega 3 fatty acids (10 ml fish oil) will very likely provide protection from MS. For children over ten, a vitamin D supplement of 2000 IU and 4 grams of omega 3 fatty acids (20 ml fish oil) are recommended. The most convenient way to get an adequate supply of both these nutrients is to use flavoured cod liver oil.

In addition to Vitamin D and fish oil, following the nutritional strategies of eliminating certain foods would also be helpful in preventing MS. Plus, we've found that when the whole household supports and adopts the Best Bet Diet it is much easily for the family member with MS to follow it and stay in good health.

RECOMMENDED DAILY
REGIMEN OF SUPPLEMENTS

ESSENTIALS

- Vitamin D3: 6000–8000 IU
  This is best gotten from pills not associated with vitamin A.

- Omega 3 Essential Fatty Acids: 5–8 g of EPA+DHA
  This is best gotten from 1–2 tablespoons of fish oil (Carlson makes a good product). Cod liver oil is also an option but ensure that vitamin A content does not exceed 5000 IU. The addition of 1 tablespoon of flax oil can be of value because it contains alpha linolenic acid, a precursor to EPA and DHA.

- Calcium: 400–500 mg

- Magnesium: 300–400 mg

- Vitamin B complex: 50–100 mg

- Probiotics: 2 to 4 capsules (2 with each meal)

OPTIONAL SUPPLEMENTS

- Vitamin A: 3000 IU

- Vitamin B12: 1–2 mg

- Vitamin E (natural): 200 IU

- Zinc: 15 mg

- Copper: 1 mg

- Selenium: 100 mcg

- Iodine: 200 mcg

- Flax oil 2–3 grams

Frequently Asked Questions

Why should I consider using nutritional strategies as part of my overall effort to control the MS disease process?

There is a great deal of scientific information linking various nutritional factors to the onset and progression of MS. Many of these nutritional issues related to MS can be readily addressed and resolved by the strategies discussed in this book. Notably, many people have had great success in keeping MS well controlled by using the recommended, science-based, nutritional strategies.

How soon should I see positive results from nutritional strategies?

The length of time between starting the use of nutritional strategies and seeing positive benefits greatly varies from person to person. Many have reported obvious benefits within a month, whereas others have had to wait between 6 months and a year.

Can I eat any dairy products?

Dairy products contain proteins that activate myelin-sensitive immune cells and thus any consumption of dairy products helps to drive the MS disease process. All dairy products from milk to cheese to yogurt to butter, and including those from goats, must be completely avoided at all times. Any "cheating" on this can be very problematic. There are a number of good substitutes for dairy products available. I might note that when I go to a restaurant, I always tell the waiter I have allergies and that it is most important that my meal be completely free of dairy and gluten.

Why is gluten a problem in MS?

The biggest reason gluten is a major problem for MS is that it contains proteins which stimulate the production of zonulin. Zonulin opens both the intestinal barrier and the blood-brain barrier and the failure of these barriers is a key part of the MS disease process. The complete avoidance of gluten at all times is essential. Notably, a number of neurological problems are directly related to gluten ingestion.

Should I use salt?

A variety of scientific studies have shown that excess sodium contributes to the MS disease process. The best way to avoid excess sodium is to limit sodium intake to less than 1 gram (1000 mg) a day (average Canadian intake is 3500 mg/day). This will involve reducing salt intake as much as possible. Most products have sodium content listed on the package and it is important to avoid products with excessive sodium.

How much vitamin D should I take?

One wants to maintain a blood level of vitamin D of 100–150 nmol/l (40-60 ng/ml) to ensure all systems have access to required vitamin D. A daily supplement of 4000–5000 IU of vitamin D3 should be sufficient for most people and the cost is less than a dime a day.

What types of fats are best to eat?

There are four different types of fat with two being potentially problematic and two being of help. There is solid scientific evidence that excess saturated fat and omega 6 fat contribute to MS worsening. Monounsaturated fat and omega 3 fat are beneficial for MS. The key to fat intake is a balance of the four fat types. For a reasonable intake of 80 grams of fat a day, 40 g of monounsaturated (olive oil best), 20 g of saturated, 13 g of omega 6, and 7 g of omega 3 (fish oil mainly) is an ideal balance.

What are the best sources of anti-oxidants?

It is important to combat excess oxidation which is part of the MS inflammatory process. Most persons with MS have been shown to be deficient in anti-oxidants. The best way to ensure adequate anti-oxidants is to consume lots of vegetables and fruits, the more the better. Anti-oxidant supplements also can help.

How can I make sure I have a good gut flora?

Research has demonstrated that adverse elements in the gut flora are part of the MS disease process by way of altering immune responses and increasing gut wall permeability. Our nutritional recommendations, which include pre-biotics and probiotic supplements, will ensure a healthy gut flora is established and maintained.

Are there any prevention strategies for MS?

Given there is a genetic component of MS, anyone with a family member with MS should definitely look at ways to reduce the risk of MS. The easiest way to prevent MS is to ensure adequate vitamin D (4000–6000 IU/d) (1000–4000 IU for children) and to use other nutritional strategies such as the avoidance of dairy and gluten. Ensuring a healthy gut flora would also greatly lessen the chance of developing MS.

How do I avoid substantial weight loss on the BBD?

Some people experience weight loss on the BBD and this is not a problem as long as a reasonable weight is maintained. To avoid unwanted weight loss, one can eat more of the allowed foods (i.e. nuts which are high in good fats) and use more extra virgin olive oil on the vegetables.

Living Proof

Best Bet Diet Success Stories

As we mentioned in the forward, our son Mathew's diagnosis with MS is what led us to develop the Best Bet Diet and start our charity Direct-MS. We are so proud of Mathew for his commitment to diet and exercise and how he has controlled his symptoms for over 24 years since his diagnosis. Mathew has decided to share his story around the world to help others with MS. He has developed a website MShope.com where he freely provides the strategies he has used to live a drug-free, healthy life.

Being a filmmaker, he has also made an award winning documentary called Living Proof about his experiences with MS and his journey to find answers and hope. The response from the documentary has been extremely positive and Mathew has received many heart warming messages about how the film has made an impact on many lives.

You will find many inspiring testimonials in this section of the book written by people affected by MS who have greatly benefited from using nutritional strategies. It is these stories that keep us motivated to share information about the Best Bet Diet and we hope they will inspire you to implement and stick to the nutritional strategies and to stay in the best health possible.

"one of the most affecting
movies ... this year."
— Steve Gravestock, Senior Programmer - TIFF

"consistently moves and surprises"
— Patrick Mullen, POV Magazine

"a vitally needed warning about
the state of modern medicine"
— Steve Kopian, Unseen Films

"a journey both
personal and political"
— Lauren Wissot, Filmmaker Magazine

"A heartbreaking ... quest"
— Steve Gow, Original Cin

"an incendiary, disciplined and
heartbreaking exposé..."
— Magali Simard, TIFF Canada Film Curator

His son has an autoimmune disease.
He might have the answer.

LIVING PROOF

Does the establishment care?

SPOTLIGHT PRODUCTIONS PRESENTS IN ASSOCIATION WITH CANADA MEDIA FUND AND ALBERTA MEDIA FUND A FILM BY MATT EMBRY "LIVING PROOF"

SCORE BY WILLIAM BAIRD SOUND RECORDIST/MIXER ADAM NAUGLER ASSOCIATE PRODUCERS ADAM NAUGLER STEVE DIERKENS STORY EDITOR TODD LANGILLE EDITED BY JORDAN BOSCH DEAN EVANS ALLAN THRUSH STORY EDITOR MIKE KRAFT DIRECTOR OF PHOTOGRAPHY PATRICK McLAUGHLIN

Canada Media Fund Alberta EXECUTIVE PRODUCERS MANJIT MINHAS RAVINDER MINHAS JYOTI AULUCK PRODUCED BY MATT EMBRY TYLER McLEOD RAVINDER MINHAS DIRECTED BY MATT EMBRY spotlight productions

www.SeeLivingProof.com

"My teenage years were overloaded with typical teenage unhealthy fare. Though I was an athlete, my diet throughout high school consisted of "multiple colas a day, high dairy, high fat foods with huge amounts of mac and cheese, "not to mention" enormous quantities of chocolate milk.

I was diagnosed with multiple sclerosis in 1995 when I was 19. One day when, while kicking a basketball, my foot suddenly went numb, followed by nerve sensitivity, which quickly progressed up into my chest. A subsequent MRI revealed numerous lesions on my brain and spine.

My neurologist's predictions were vague and suggested disability in my future. However, he emphasized there was no need to consider jumping off a bridge, just yet. At that time there were no pharmaceuticals available for MS so I did not face the big question of "to use or not to use". Within a week, we had gotten hold of books by Roy Swank and Judy Graham and a common theme was that diet played a major role in MS. This gave us the first major ray of hope.

My father is a research scientist and he plunged into the MS scientific literature to understand what drives MS and how dietary factors might be involved. Based on this research, he devised a science-based, dietary regimen that subsequently became known as the Best Bet Diet. The basics included no dairy, no gluten, no refined sugars, no legumes, low saturated fat, lots of vegetables and fruits, as well as various supplements.

I recognized I only had two choices: radically change my diet or end up in a wheelchair. Happily, my MS symptoms disappeared after about 4 months on the diet and over the next few years the only times I experienced the return of some symptoms were once when I had a bad flu. In 1999, my father realized that vitamin D was a big factor in MS and I started taking 4000 IU a day. Over the last 24 years I have been symptom-free, and I have to emphasize "You gotta go all in" and that there are no cheat days.

To me, there is no doubt that my nutritional changes have played a very significant part in keeping MS in remission, but I would add that so too have physical fitness and mindfulness. It's YOUR health and YOUR responsibility. It's on YOU. The choices YOU make are the ones that set the course for YOU and your future. My Dad once told me 'You are either getting better or you are getting worse.' I have made the decision to get better every day and with every meal. I hope you will do the same."

– Mathew Embry

❝ I was diagnosed with MS in 2000. Eighteen years on I ran the London marathon fuelled only by the Best Bet Diet.

On the build-up to my diagnosis (1997–2000) I was experiencing a range of symptoms from optic neuritis to 'disconnected legs', tingling sensations and severe fatigue. My mood changed dramatically and depression set in. When I managed to lift my head from the shock and fear of what was happening, I began to research MS and what I could do personally to take control. The doctors only seemed able (and willing) to prescribe drugs that claim to treat the symptoms without reference to the cause.

In 2000 I was fortunate enough to find a doctor here in Scotland who practiced 'Environmental and nutritional medicine' and after a battery of tests I embarked on a highly personalised supplement and diet regime. This had an immediate effect of lifting my mood, clearing the 'brain fog', reducing the tingling and lifting my energy levels. Around the same time my wife found Ashton's website and the Best Bet Diet. Scotland and Canada are the MS capitals of the world. My personalised approach mirrored the Best Bet Diet in every respect. Reassurance in itself!

Two years on the dietary approach had turned my life around. Infuriated and inspired by the failure of the medical profession (supported by many in the MS 'support' organizations), I cycled 1003 miles from Seattle to San Francisco to raise awareness and funds for the dietary approach to MS. I had the great pleasure of inviting Ashton and his wife Joan to Scotland to speak on their groundbreaking research. Information on the dietary approach is now given to all new MS patients at Scottish hospitals. This evidence based, scientifically authentic approach is helping to establish the Best Bet Diet, Direct-MS and MS Hope as a 'go-to' source of help for those of us living with MS and those who support us.

Nearly 20 years on from diagnosis, Ashton's work and the Best Bet Diet continue to keep me (and so many others I've connected with) well and happy. Last week I ran my latest half marathon. In the face of a devastating diagnosis the Best Bet Diet lets you do the most important thing of all, take personal charge of your future. ❞

– Alan Caldwell

" I am a 54-year-old male and I was formally diagnosed with multiple sclerosis at the age of 28 in 1992. Initially, I was diagnosed with relapsing-remitting MS but this soon progressed into secondary progressive MS. Being of Ukrainian descent, my diet was premised upon wheat and dairy with ample saturated fats. In 1996, upon reading The Best Bet Diet essay, I revised my diet to exclude certain dietary proteins. Incorporating the Best Bet Diet necessitated fundamental changes in my food consumption. It was with great fortune that my spouse also bought into this strategy as she was the primary food preparer. Her commitment to ensuring my dietary restrictions were satisfied contributed greatly to my improved health and independence.

Very soon after adopting the BBD my digestive processes improved considerably. I achieved consistent and proper bowel movements and I was no longer plagued by intestinal gas and bloating. Within weeks of implementing these changes, I noticed improvements in my well-being and mental abilities such as memory, comprehension and acuity that I attribute to a reduction in nerve inflammation. My oppressive chronic fatigue was also reduced significantly as was the numbness that was present throughout my body.

Overall the BBD provided stability in the progression of my MS. My improvements and stability allowed me to return to the work force, after a three-year hiatus, and to embark on having what turned out to be a family of three children.

I was, and still am, hampered by deficiencies that I attribute to nerve damage. The diet revision has not improved my right leg impairments which affect my mobility profoundly. Despite this inability to walk properly, I continue to feel well and maintain an optimistic perspective because my disease has not progressed since I adopted the dietary measures. "

– Nick Topolnyski

" I had my first MS exacerbation in 1997 but I was not diagnosed with MS in December 2015. My symptoms before starting an anti-inflammatory diet included numbness, tingling, pain, impaired vision, skin pain, phantom sensations and incontinence.

When I was finally diagnosed with MS, Melissa and I had spent ten years together developing many rituals around dinner. We planned each meal, prepared it together, and always ate the same thing. Changing my diet following my diagnosis in the winter of 2015 meant challenging our dinner rituals. At first, I withdrew, becoming focused on what foods I could and couldn't eat … and I did so at the expense of our shared sense of having dinner together. As the diet became more natural to us, Melissa and I began to find ways to share dinner once again. We roasted vegetables, made soups, and steamed veggies of various kinds. Melissa adapted without completely abandoning the foods she needed and loved, and I sometimes ate things that weren't on her plate. Most importantly, we came to enjoy dinner together once again. Starting a new diet can seem like a challenge of will power. But it can also challenge relationships, and to succeed at this diet it's been important for me to have support, understanding, and commitment at multiple levels.

After strictly following my anti-inflammatory diet for over three years now, it's become a natural and vital part of how we live. Results from religiously following an anti-inflammatory diet, reducing stress, increasing rest, and increasing vitamin D levels: No new exacerbations and no new lesions. I am currently leading a very physically active life and enjoy full mobility. I have some residual symptoms from my many years of exacerbations, but I see them as part of who I am. "

– Spencer Schaffner

" My earliest years in life were spent on a farm in rural Ontario where I developed a fondness for dairy products and sugary treats. I was diagnosed with MS in 1992 at the age of 24 while doing graduate studies. I continued consuming a highly inflammatory, non-compliant diet for many years, even though I had read Dr. Embry's writing in 1997 or so. I lacked discipline back then and paid a heavy price with my health. Months after CCSVI treatment in 2010 many of the typical symptoms of MS slowly returned – the brain fog, fatigue, lack of motivation. Since adopting the Best Bet Diet and other lifestyle changes, I have experienced a major shift in fatigue levels, improved ability to think, and increased motivation and ability to exercise. Diet was the game-changer that I needed to be a healthier me.

I've always been impressed with Direct-MS and MS Hope because of the free advice that they offer. It's easy to live a healthy, compliant life without spending hundreds or thousands of dollars – all it takes is an ounce of imagination sprinkled with a dash of creativity! "

– Christopher Alkenbrack

" I was diagnosed with RRMS in 1997 at age 21. My first symptoms included transverse myelitis which caused ascending numbness, starting on the pads of my feet and eventually reaching my ribs and aggravating my phrenic nerve causing severe abdominal pain. I also experienced two bouts of optic neuritis later in life and I have had numerous relapses since diagnosis. I would get home from working an office job and fall asleep on the couch. When I went to bed, I would struggle to fall asleep and when I did, I couldn't stay asleep. I was tired all the time and frequently sick. My family life was affected. My friendships were affected. My livelihood was affected.

I wanted so desperately to continue my life, "business as usual". And so that's what I told everyone for nearly 2 decades. Yes, I was diagnosed, but I'm not going to let that slow me down. But it wasn't business as usual. It was scary. It was uncertain. It was at times painful and depressing. It became apparent that not only were my decisions and the direction that I had been given endangering my health, but in fact I was a ticking time-bomb, heading down a very dark path.

I first heard about the Best Bet Diet while researching treatment alternatives online and started the diet in 2015. A month after starting the BBD program, I had my energy back, my mood and outlook improved, my wife of now 13 years said she'd never seen me better. The most difficult aspect, as well as the most surprising, was the backlash I faced from friends, some family members, coworkers and social media followers. Part of adopting this diet, fitness plan and lifestyle, will be testing one's resolve. To me it was important to keep things in perspective. Not having cheese and dairy is easier than not being able to walk upstairs. Avoiding gluten and processed foods is far easier than life in a wheelchair. Being questioned about not consuming refined sugar or having dessert pales in comparison to not playing outside with our kids...these are the stakes that we are up against when living with MS. We know this and now we also know that we can alter the course of this disease. We owe it to ourselves. We owe it to our loved ones.

It is never to late to start. It is never to late to help a loved one start. There is literally no down-side to following this proven program. I am not overstating when I say this program saved my life and my relationships. My results since beginning the BBD Program speak for themselves. My EDSS score has dropped from 3.5 to 2.5 and my last two MRIs have shown stability and no new lesions. I am in the gym daily, I follow the plan; I'm myself again and I have a positive outlook. "

– Mark Bennett

" This July 2019 I will be celebrating my thirty years of primary progressive MS (PPMS) at age 84 and in relatively good health for an old guy. Naturally, there's a story behind it. My parents immigrated from Poland and I was born in America. I was a thin child (now a thin adult) that disturbed my parents because in the old country being thin meant sickness. Hence, I was brought up with a typical Polish diet, high saturated fat, dairy, eggs, rye bread, etc. that I enjoyed.

About a decade before my PPMS diagnosis I became interested in diet because my cholesterol level was over 300. I immediately took corrective action and eliminated eggs and reduced saturated fat from my diet. As the years progressed, I eliminate meat since it was not tasty.

I am an exercise fanatic, in fact, I'm an obsessive, compulsive, neurotic nut case, and noticed walking issues after exercising. And in 1989 I was diagnosed with PPMS. As an engineer I now had a problem I had to solve. My family physician provided me with sage advice. "I don't know anything about MS, but I advise you to work on your overall wellness." Finding data on MS was a challenge. I retired in 1994 due to draining fatigue.

In 1996, the internet started to bloom, and I learned about Ashton Embry's BBD plan and was excited. It is based on data, an engineer's dream. I adopted the plan, gave up my favorite food, dairy and lost about 35 pounds.

The rest is history. With help of trainers I learned to walk 99% perfect gait of two miles and was able to swim three miles nonstop. I recently contacted one of the senior fitness instructors with my weekly exercise regime asking if I'm over doing it. Her response was yes, and she suggested I should reduce my exercise. My swimming from 1 hr. to ½ hour, reduce weight lifting reps from 50 to 18–20; bike ride from 45 to 20–25 minutes. I think it's a reasonable plan for an old fart with PPMS.

Finally, think diet, exercise and attitude. And for an old guy I'm doing okay and still exercise daily. "

– Irwin Mortman

" In the fall of 2017, our healthy, active, 15-year-old daughter began getting daily migraine headaches and then suddenly went blind in one eye. In the months following, she experienced Bell's Palsy, a zapping sensation down her spine, and random numbness and weakness that left her unable to walk or use her arms for days. With no family history of MS, we had no idea what to expect with this disease and we were terrified. We were open to any and all advice and were especially interested in hearing success stories about people with no MS symptoms long term. We were determined to do whatever it took to make sure our daughter followed the same path.

Very quickly we found MS Hope and the Embry family as Matt Embry's film, Living Proof, had just debuted at the Toronto International Film Festival. Seeing that film was life changing for us and literally gave us hope for the first time. We really appreciated the amount of science behind the Best Bet Diet. Knowing exactly why we had to eliminate certain foods made it so much easier to stick to the protocol with no cheat days.

We are extremely happy, proud and thankful to say that our daughter is currently a year and a half completely symptom and relapse free on the Best Bet Diet. This diet has given our teenager her life back. Our whole family now follows the BBD and we have no plan to ever change our new way of eating. Health is a great motivator.

Thank you to the Embry family for sharing their knowledge and protocol so openly and freely. We can't imagine where we would be without them. "

– Anonymous

"   The Best Bet Diet is amazing, but so different from all the foods I used to eat before taking this very healthy step in 2018. I was diagnosed with MS in 2001 and I continued to eat what I had always eaten, never thinking if some food was good or bad for me. My only rule was that if some food was tasty and that is what I ate. My diet until 2018, included lots of milk products (my very favourite milk chocolate), red meat, legumes of all kinds such as peanuts, and bean and pea stew. I also enjoyed warm wheat bread and all kinds of sugar-containing biscuits, waffles, candies etc. I had no awareness how bad these foods could be for my health.

Awareness came when I watched the documentary LIVING PROOF by Matt Embry, and I realized you can never be sure if or when your MS will come back into your life. I learned that it is better to eat healthy food in order to have a healthy future, and hopefully—no MS. I began with the BBD, creating my own ANTI-MS menu every single day. All the terrible fatigue, swollen stomach, dizziness, heaviness in my legs etc. have disappeared from my life and I have been light-of-foot and symptom-free for more than a year now.

I have been strictly following the Best Bet Diet and I replaced all my favorite but very problematic foods with healthy substitutes. I replaced the cow's milk with almond/hazelnut milk and combine it with buckwheat muesli for a great breakfast! My biggest problem was to completely avoid sugar, my very favourite milk chocolate, and wheat bread. I had to totally change my thinking and attitude and tell myself I really don't need my so-called "favourite foods".

Instead of chocolate, I eat sweet fresh fruits and enjoy fruit/veggie juice. When drinking tea, I use stevia instead of sugar and avoiding sugar has given me much more energy. Instead of red meat, I eat more fatty fish and healthy baked vegetables. I replaced my old favourite peanuts with hazelnuts and walnuts. I have also found a wonderful replacement for my favourite wheat bread by baking my own gluten-free bread from buckwheat flour.

Importantly, I eat all these foods in moderation which is another healthy rule for a healthy life. I have discovered that healthy foods can be very delicious, and that healthy food recipes can be endless. It is essential to keep the faith and to stay positive! Notably, positive thinking, like healthy food, is healing too! "

– Victor Alexsiev

Meal Strategies

Getting Started

The aim of this diet is to stop the consumption of foods whose molecular structures are so similar to the myelin in our own bodies that they could initiate the autoimmune process. The foods that have been identified as problematic include dairy, gluten and legumes. Eggs and yeast are allowed in limited quantities as long as the individual does not show any allergic reaction to them. Initially this diet appears very limiting in our present diet culture but hopefully the following tips and strategies will make the transition to new dietary habits easier.

Avoid foods that cause an allergic reaction

Foods can cause an allergic reaction in the gut and this entails the activation of immune cells which produce both IgE and IgG4 antibodies. Such inflammatory reactions can lead to a leaky gut which results in food protein fragments passing into the circulatory system where they can cause autoimmune reactions.

The best way to identify immune-reactive foods is an ELISA (enzyme-linked immunosorbent assay) blood test. This test measures the amounts of IgE and IgG4 antibodies produced when a blood sample is challenged with a given food protein. The advantages of this type of test is that it is non-invasive ("in vitro"), easy to administer, relatively cheap, and can cover most common foods. Such testing can be facilitated by a naturopathic or functional medicine doctor.

EXCLUDED FOODS

DAIRY

Cow's milk and all dairy products and also lactose free products are excluded. The concern with dairy products is the protein fraction of the cow's milk.

Fragments of dairy protein closely resemble parts of myelin proteins. Specific immune cells that attack dairy proteins also attack myelin proteins. Dairy proteins cause an MS-like disease in laboratory animals.

AVOID:
- Milk and all derivatives of milk
- Lactaid
- Cheese
- Butter
- Cottage cheese
- Yogurt
- Ice cream
- Milk Proteins – It is important to read food labels to make sure that milk protein is avoided. Milk Proteins include:
  - Casein
  - Lactalbumin, lactoglobulin, bovine albumin, and gamma goblin
  - Whey, caseinates, skim milk powder and milk solids
- Goat's milk and sheep's milk and any cheeses etc made from these are also excluded because they also contain proteins that must be avoided.
- Soy milk is not allowed as a milk substitute as it is derived from soybeans, which are legumes.

GLUTEN

The biggest reason gluten is a major problem for MS is that it contains a protein called zonulin. This protein opens up both the intestinal barrier and the blood-brain barrier and the failure of these barriers is a key part of the MS disease process.

Notably, several neurological problems are directly related to gluten ingestion. The complete avoidance of gluten at all times is essential.

AVOID:

- Wheat
- Rye
- Barley
- Oats
- White and whole-wheat flours
- Durham flour
- Triticale
- Bulgar
- Spelt
- Kamut
- Soy flour must be excluded as it is made from soybeans and cannot be used because it is a legume.
- Cereal – Even gluten-free cereals are filled with sugar so it's best to opt for nuts, seeds and fruit for a breakfast alternative.

LEGUMES

Legumes can potentially contribute to the MS disease process in two ways:

1. Legumes contain proteins called lectins and these proteins contribute to increased leakiness of the gut wall. This in turn allows proteins to pass through the gut wall and initiate autoimmune reactions.

2. Legumes contain proteins that closely resemble self-proteins in the central nervous system, and these can activate myelin-sensitive immune cells.

AVOID:
- All beans (adzuki beans, black beans, broad beans, fava beans, field beans, garbanzo beans, horse beans, kidney beans, lima beans, mung beans, navy beans, pinto beans, navy beans pinto beans, red beans, yellow and green string beans, white beans)
- Black-eyed peas
- Carob
- Chickpeas
- Lentils
- Peas
- Miso
- Peanuts and peanut butter
- Snow peas
- Sugar snap peas
- Soybeans and all soybean products, including tofu – There are many products that contain soybean, so it is important to read labels to exclude soy from your diet.

CORN AS A CONCERN

Those sensitive to wheat are often sensitive to other cereal grains rice, oats and especially to corn. It is recommended to limit the use of these grains. Even though corn flour and cornmeal are wheat and gluten-free it is advised to use other gluten-free products. Cornstarch is often used as a thickener, but arrowroot and potato flour and rice flour can be substituted for this purpose. The importance of reading labels to identify corn is very important as it is used a variety of products (margarine, baking mixes, baking powder, candy, marshmallows, bourbon and some whiskies).

EGG RESTRICTIONS

Eggs are one of the most highly allergic foods. If you have sensitivity to eggs restrict them. Products containing eggs, egg yolk, egg white, egg albumen or albumen need to be avoided. Again, it is important to read labels. It is advised to use eggs only in moderation, no more than two a week.

YEAST RESTRICTIONS

Yeast is another highly allergic food and needs to be limited if one is allergic to yeast.

REDUCE SUGAR

Greatly reduce all sugar intake. Sugar promotes the growth and expansion of bad gut bacteria in the microbiome. An unhealthy microbiome increases gut leakiness and also fosters pro-inflammatory immune reactions.

REDUCE SALT

High sodium intake has been shown to be pro-inflammatory and associated with MS. Table salt is the main source of sodium and is found in many packaged foods. Ensure your sodium intake does not exceed 1000 mg/day. Notably average intake in North America is 3500 mg/day.

ASPARTAME AND OTHER ARTIFICIAL SWEETENERS

It is well established that artificial sweeteners are very detrimental for the microbiome resulting in a leaky gut and inflammation.

BUTTER AND FAT

A proper balance of the four types of fat is very important for establishing a well-regulated immune system. It is important to keep saturated fat intake low.

AVOID:
• Butter and lard must be completely avoided as they are pure saturated fat.
• Any product with trans-fats, which are highly inflammatory, must be avoided.

Butter Alternatives

The best fat type to use for cooking is extra virgin olive oil which is primarily monounsaturated fat and is a good immune regulator. Margarine can be used sparingly and should contain mainly omega 6 and monounsaturated fat. Many margarines contain milk products and have to be strictly avoided. There are a few dairy-free margarines. Flax seed oil, walnut oil, canola oil, mustard seed oil and avocado oil may also be used but are not suitable if they are heated too high so as to create trans-fats.

EXCLUDED BEVERAGES, FOODS AND ADDITIVES

AVOID:
• Malt-containing beverages:
    ○ Postum
    ○ Ovaltine
    ○ Beers and ales
• Whisky and Beer have gluten in them.

KITCHEN CLEANSE

Once you have committed to embrace the diet there are a few key strategies that are very helpful.

• Remove all the groceries and products that are not diet friendly (gluten, dairy, legumes and any foods that cause allergic reactions) from your kitchen.

• When you go shopping do not buy items that are not on the Best Bet Diet, so you won't be tempted with these foods in the house.

• If you must cook for others in the household, have your own cupboard to store foods that meet the diet criteria.

• Visit a local health food store and your favourite grocery store and look for products that are Best Bet Diet friendly. You will be pleasantly surprised by the variety of products out there.

Food Substitutes

It is important to completely eliminate the foods to avoid which were discussed earlier. To help with this, we have listed some acceptable food substitutes for the common foods to avoid such as dairy, gluten and legumes. Such substitute products can be found in health food stores and sometimes in the major grocery stores.

As was emphasized, all dairy (cow, goat, lactose free) products must be strictly avoided. Acceptable cow's milk substitutes include almond milk, rice milk and to a lesser extent coconut milk. Good substitutes for cheese are numerous, tapioca-based products made by Daiya. Various, non-dairy Parmesan cheese substitutes are in health food stores. Be sure to check the labels to ensure there is no dairy or soy in any of the products you find.

Substitutes for dairy-based ice cream are widely available and include rice-based and coconut-based ice cream and gelato. Avoid soy-based ice cream products and always check the ingredients of a seemingly suitable product for any soy or gluten.

Yogurt is a useful food given its probiotic qualities. Dairy-based yogurts must be avoided but coconut, almond, and cashew-based yogurts are popping up all over the place. Importantly, they contain that same great "healthy bacteria."

Gluten, which is in wheat, barley and rye, is found in many products and it is essential to always read ingredient labels to ensure avoidance. Notably, there are good gluten-free substitutes for the common gluten-containing products. Rice-based products, from breads to pastas to pizza crusts, are widely available in health food and grocery stores. Gluten-free flours are readily attainable, and it is best to avoid those which are corn-based.

A good replacement for soy sauce (legume product often with gluten) is coconut aminos, a delicious, soy and gluten-free sauce made from coconut sap. It is dark, rich, salty and slightly sweet in flavour.

Another legume product to avoid is peanut butter and excellent substitutes are almond butter and cashew butter, which are found in health food and grocery stores.

Anyone with an egg allergy should use a commercial egg replacer. For example, a common one is made of mixture of potato starch, tapioca flour and leavening agents. These products are found mainly in health food stores.

As discussed earlier, it is important to have a moderate intake of sodium (Na) (<1000 mg/d). Table salt (NaCl) is the main source of sodium and it is important to read labels which usually includes the sodium content of a serving size. One way to help with this is to use a potassium-based salt product. Various herbs, spices and lemon pepper can also be used as substitutes when cooking.

MILK ALTERNATIVES

Rice Milk
A non-dairy, fat free milk derived from rice that can be used as a good dairy substitute. It is light and naturally sweet and can be successfully used in most recipes. For some, processed rice milk may be a problem because it can be filtered using a barley enzyme.

Almond Milk
A tasty, nutritious milk alternative. It is low in calories and sugar and high in calcium, vitamin E and vitamin D. You can use almond milk in any way that you would use regular dairy milk.

Coconut Milk
The liquid that comes from the grated pulp of a mature coconut. The opacity and rich taste of coconut milk are due to its high oil content, which is saturated fat. It is best to limit coconut milk due to its high saturated fat.

Hazelnut Milk
A plant-based alternative and is gluten, lactose, and soy-free and contains no saturated fat.

WHEAT-FREE AND GLUTEN-FREE FLOURS

There are a wide variety of gluten-free flours to choose from. Most can be found at health food stores and grocery stores. The following information hopefully will be a resource for those choosing to bake. For some people all grains may be problematic.

Amaranth Flour
The seeds from this plant are milled into flour. It is high in fiber, protein, calcium and iron. This flour has a naturally nutty flavour. It can be used for baking bread.

Arrowroot Flour
This root is ground into white, fine powdery flour. It is used as a thickener in sauces and has no flavour.

Brown Rice Flour
This flour comes from brown rice and contains the "bran" of the rice. Because it contains the bran of the rice, it offers more nutrients such as iron, calcium, niacin and thiamin than white rice flour. Due to the oil in the bran of the rice, this flour should be refrigerated.

Buckwheat Flour
Although it has "wheat" in the name, this flour is gluten-free. This flour has a strong flavour and can be used in combination with rice flour to make pancakes and other baked goods.

Cassava
Is high in starch, gluten-free and often used to thicken recipes. Cassava flour can be used as 1:1 substitute in recipes for other flours.

Millet
This flour is harvested from an ancient wild grass. When cooked, millet looks a lot like rice, and in fact can be used exactly like rice as a "starch" side dish, in soups, as a hot cereal, etc. Millet tastes best if you prepare it as follows: The millet will be hulled when you buy it and will look like tiny birdseed. Wash it first in a bowl, drain and let it dry. Then heat a dry skillet and "toast" the millet over a high heat, stirring so that it all gets toasted and doesn't burn. This step improves the flavour. The ratio of millet to water is 1 cup millet to 3 cups water. Heat the water to boiling, slowly stir in the toasted millet (if you add it all at once it will boil over), return it to a boil, reduce the heat and cook in a covered pot about 40 minutes until the water is all absorbed. The little grains pop open like popcorn and will look almost like fluffy cooked rice.

Potato Flour

This is not the same as potato starch. This flour is made from cooked, dried and ground potatoes. It is used as a thickener and adds moisture to batters and dough to prevent crumbling.

Quinoa

This flour originates from South America. It has a bitter flavour and is a very good source of protein. It contains more nutritional value than most gluten containing grains. Because of its bitter flavour it is used in small amounts in baked goods.

Tapioca Flour

This flour provides the spongy texture to gluten-free breads. It is a white, soft flour that comes from the cassava root. This flour does not provide any flavour to baking.

White Rice Flour

This flour is an all-purpose, gluten-free flour. It can be used to make bread, cookies, and muffins and can be used as a thickener. It comes from milling polished rice, which makes it fairly bland.

RICE AND PASTA SUBSTITUTES

Even though rice and rice pasta are Best Bet Diet friendly, reducing carbs and adding more vegetables is always better! Here are a few delicious substitutes:

Cauliflower Rice
Can be used for practically any dish that calls for brown or white rice.

How to Make Cauliflower Rice
1. Wash and thoroughly dry 1 large head of cauliflower, then remove all greens and the core.

2. If using a box grater, cut the cauliflower into large chunks and use the medium-sized holes (to grate into "rice"). If using a food processor, cut into small pieces and use the grater attachment to grate the cauliflower into "rice".

3. Optional: Transfer to a clean towel or paper towel and press to remove any excess moisture, which can make your dish soggy.

4. Once you have your cauliflower rice, it's easy to cook (or enjoy raw). Simply sauté in a large skillet over medium heat in 1 tablespoon oil. Cover with a lid so the cauliflower steams and becomes more tender. Cook for a total of 5-8 minutes, then season as desired (such as with coconut aminos or salt and pepper).

5. Use cauliflower rice in recipes that call for rice, such as stir fries or fried rice. Store leftovers in the refrigerator up to 5 days. Store uncooked cauliflower rice in the freezer up to 1 month.

Zucchini Noodles (Zoodles)
A tasty noodle that can be used for numerous healthy gluten-free recipes. You can make them by using a spiralizer, julienne peeler, or a mandoline.

How to Make Zoodles
1. With a Spiralizer
   Using a spiralizer, you simply cut off the ends of a zucchini, place it next to the blade and spin. In less than 8 seconds you'll have spiral sliced the entire zucchini. Other vegetables that can be made into "noodles" are carrots, sweet potato, apples, pears.

2. Julienne Peeler

    A julienne peeler is a peeler with serrated teeth.

3. The Mandoline

    The mandoline creates julienne noodles that are slightly thicker than a peeler but does it in half the time. The mandoline creates the best flat zucchini pasta and allows you to vary the thickness.

How to Cook Zucchini Noodles

Zucchini are comprised of 95 percent water. When you cook them, you may end up with a soggy, mushy mess of watery noodles—just by cooking one minute too long. When you're cooking zoodles, the intention is simply to heat them up and not really to "cook".

1. Eat zucchini noodles raw

    The best way to get the crispiest, most al dente noodles is to keep them raw. Mix with your favourite ingredients and serve. For example, the zoodles can be mixed with a cold avocado cucumber sauce or pesto sauce. If your zucchini is room temperature, simply mixing the noodles with a hot sauce, like a spaghetti sauce, warms them to the perfect temperature.

2. How to microwave zucchini noodles

    Place zucchini noodles in a microwave-safe dish and cook for one minute. Depending on the number of noodles used, the noodles may need to cook longer, at 30-second increments to prevent over-cooking. Then, divide the noodles between serving plates and top with your favourite sauce.

3. How to sauté Zucchini Noodles

    Add one tablespoon of olive oil or avocado oil to a pan and sauté for 1–2 minutes.

4. How to boil Zucchini Noodles

    Boil a pot of water, toss in your zucchini noodles and cook for one minute. Once noodles have cooked, drain the noodles in a colander and serve. Blot them with a paper towel before serving.

Spaghetti Squash

The perfect base for things like lasagna, pasta dishes, soups, and more.

How to Cook Spaghetti Squash

1 large spaghetti squash
1 tablespoon oil
1 pinch sea salt

1. Preheat oven to 400°F and line a large rimmed baking sheet or baking dish with parchment paper or foil.

2. Cook the spaghetti squash in the microwave for 2–3 minutes to soften before cutting. Carefully halve spaghetti squash lengthwise using a sharp knife.

3. Use an ice cream scoop (or sharp spoon) to scrape out the seeds.

4. Brush the interior with oil and sprinkle with salt. Place cut-side down on baking sheet. Roast for 45 minutes, or until a knife easily pierces the skin and flesh. Remove from oven and set aside.

5. For a moister squash, omit the oil and instead add just enough water to cover the bottom of your baking sheet or baking dish and bake at 400°F until a knife easily pierces the exterior (about 35–45 minutes).

6. Once slightly cool, flip squash flesh-side up and use a fork to scrape out the strings.

7. Then you add tomato sauce, salad dressing, pesto, or any other sauce you'd add to pasta. Or you could also top the spaghetti squash with a coconut curry or stew, like you'd do with rice.

Cooking Terms

Here is a very basic list of cooking terms and techniques to make it easier to end up with successful recipes.

Bake
To cook with dry heat in an oven. Technically, roasting refers to meat or vegetables, while baking refers to casseroles, breads and sweet things.

Beat
To combine foods thoroughly to incorporate air. It makes mixtures lighter. Use an electric beater, a whisk or a wooden spoon, depending on the ingredients.

Blanch
To immerse a vegetable or fruit in boiling water for a minute, draining and plunging into ice water to stop the cooking. They are now ready for a second cooking.

Blend
To smoothly combine several ingredients either by hand or in a food processor or blender.

Boil
To bring liquid to the point that large bubbles form and you can see steam. Use your highest heat.

Braise
To cook meats, fish or vegetables in liquid in a heavy pan with a heavy lid usually in the oven.

Chop
To cut ingredients into even-sized pieces.

Cream
To combine two mixtures so they appear as one. By creaming butter and sugar together, you beat in air to make your baking lighter.

Dice
To cut up in small squares for even cooking. The size varies according to the recipe, but generally ranges from a quarter-inch to two inches.

Fold
To mix a lighter mixture gently into a heavier one to retain volume and lightness. Use a large spoon. Stir a spoonful of the lighter mixture (often egg whites) into the base to lighten it, then cut and fold in the remaining mixture. In professional kitchens, chefs often use their hands.

Instant Pot
Instant Pot is a multi-cooker that does the job of a slow cooker, electric pressure cooker, rice cooker, steamer, yogurt maker, sauté/browning pan, and warming pot. It speeds up cooking 2–10 times and produces nutritious healthy food.

Julienne
To cut into matchstick-size lengths. A mandolin is useful for this.

Mince

To chop ingredients into tiny pieces.

Poaching

Poaching tenderizes food and keeps it moist. Place the food in a pan on the stove and immerse the food in a liquid with no added fat (water, juice or stock for example). Cover the pan and simmer the liquid gently (never boil the liquid rapidly). Herbs may be added to the liquid for flavour. To create a sauce, remove the poached food and reduce the poaching liquid and this can be thickened using a thickening agent (rice flour). Eggs, fish and other tender ingredients are often poached so they do not break apart.

Reduce

To boil down a stock or sauce for maximum flavour. The best reductions are made with homemade stock, but if you do not have any, use a low-salt version. Saltiness increases as you reduce a liquid.

Sauté

Sautéing is a quick cooking method, which sears the surface and browns foods. The basic idea is to quickly sear the outside of the food with heat and oil. Use a large, shallow sided pan over medium to high heat. Use a small amount of oil and heat it (do not let it smoke). If the foods brown too quickly, carefully add a tablespoon or two of water and continue cooking until the water evaporates. Stir the foods or shake the pan frequently to prevent the food from sticking. Non-stick sautéing minimizes the oil use. Using a non-stick pan allows you to sauté fish in a few drops of oil.

Sear

To brown meat in a hot pan with hot oil over high heat to seal in the juices. It takes only a couple of minutes per side. The recipe is then finished in the oven or on top of the stove.

Simmer

To cook in liquid just below boiling point. The bubbles are small and there is very little steam.

Slow Cooking

Once the food goes in the pot, the food cooks many hours, sometimes for 12 hours, depending on the recipe. You can leave the slow cooker operating while you are away from home all day. The ingredients simmer slowly until they are rich, mellow and extremely tender.

Steaming

Steaming is a desirable method of cooking vegetables; steam them using a stainless-steel basket in a covered pot or bamboo steamers (stacked in a wok or pan). Most vegetables and fish steam in less than 10 minutes. Steamed foods retain their vitamins and minerals, as well as their flavours and colors. You require a covered pot containing boiling water. The ingredients are placed in the steel basket 2–3 inches above the water. It is important to maintain the water level, so when cooking dishes for a longer time, the water level should be checked from time to time.

Wok-cooking

Wok-cooking can be used to sauté and then steam food. For stir-frying—heat 2–3 teaspoons of olive oil in a wok at high temperature. Sauté sliced chicken, fish or meat for 2–3 minutes then turn the heat down and introduce vegetables, beginning with the vegetables requiring the most cooking. Stir-fry vegetables briefly, then add a small amount of water or broth to the wok and cover it with a lid to finish the cooking by steaming.

Zest

To remove citrus peel without any white pith using a zester or a microplane grater.

Metric Equivalents

Volume	Weight	Oven Temperatures
¼ Teaspoon = 1 ml	1 oz = 30 g	250°F = 120°C
½ Teaspoon = 2 ml	2 oz = 55 g	275°F = 140°C
1 Teaspoon = 5 ml	3 oz = 85 g	300°F = 150°C
1 Tablespoon= 15 ml	4 oz = 115 g	325°F = 160°C
¼ cup = 60 ml	5 oz = 140 g	350°F = 180°C
⅓ cup = 75 ml	6 oz = 170 g	375°F = 190°C
½ cup = 125 ml	7 oz = 200 g	400°F = 200°C
⅔ cup = 150 ml	8 oz = 250 g	425°F = 220°C
¾ cup = 175 ml	16 oz = 500 g	450°F = 230°C
1 cup = 250 ml	32 oz = 1000 g	475°F = 240°C
		500°F = 260°C

Ready to Strategize

Once one becomes familiar with the foods to be excluded, it's time to create a meal strategy that meets your lifestyle. This section will provide you with various strategies and tips to get you started.

Changing to this diet will take time and it is important to understand your own personal relationship with food. Some people live to eat and enjoy the experience of foods, whereas others only eat to live. It is hoped that once you and your loved ones understand the scientific principles of this diet, everyone will work together to create MS-friendly, delicious meals. Food has often been seen as a way of showing love. What better way of showing love to loved ones than creating a diet that works best for their body.

A recipe section follows and fortunately there are many food products on the market that make this diet easy to follow. Reading the labels of various products will make it possible to add many store-bought products to your meal planning. With a few substitutions many of your favourite recipes may be used.

RECOMMENDATIONS

It will take a few months to scout out the ingredients and staples of this diet but once you are comfortable, it will be like any other meal preparation. You will be able to organize your kitchen to meet your needs and shop to make sure you have everything on hand. Many of the essentials can be found at large supermarkets or at your local health food store.

Changing to the Best Bet Diet will require planning in advance to have the necessary foods on hand for easy meal preparation.

TIPS

1. It is important to plan a full week ahead when you are grocery shopping. It can be helpful to make a meal plan for each day of the week and then develop a shopping list based on the individual meals.

2. Repetition is the enemy of sticking to the plan long term. It is important to have variety and small changes can have a positive and lasting effect on following the diet.

3. Never go grocery shopping on an empty stomach. Shopping on an empty stomach will often lead to poor purchasing decisions. Sticking to your grocery list will prevent those unwanted foods from entering your kitchen!

4. Some people set aside some time on the weekend to do some meal prep for the week to freeze or have some prepared foods on hand to take the pressure off for weekday meals.

5. When making the evening meal, cook double the amount, so you can use leftovers for breakfast or lunch the next day, or freeze for future meals.

6. The meal planning shows a variety of breakfasts; however, we have found it easiest to stick with the same breakfast every morning. Keep it simple with a smoothie or fruit and trail mix, then on the weekends you can try something more complex, when you have more time.

7. If you are finding you are losing weight, increase portion sizes depending on individual caloric needs.

MEAL IDEAS

Looking at the excluded food list may leave you wondering what you can eat. However, not to worry as there are many healthy and delicious foods included in the Best Bet Diet. Here are some ideas and examples of the healthy foods you can enjoy throughout the day.

BREAKFAST	LUNCH	DINNER	SNACKS
• Fruit (strawberries, blueberries, raspberries, cantaloupe, blackberries)	• Salads (use a variety of vegetables and meats: tuna, salmon, chicken)	• Fish (Salmon, Tuna, Talapia, Sole, Halibut)	• Fresh fruit
• Left over protein from the night before (chicken or fish)	• Fruit	• Chicken	• Raw vegetables with salsa or guacamole dip (carrots, celery, cherry tomatoes, mushrooms, broccoli, cucumbers, cauliflower)
• Smoothies	• Soup	• Seafood (shrimp, scallops, lobster, crab)	
• Rice crackers with almond butter	• Fresh vegetables	• Steamed or roasted vegetables (broccoli, cauliflower, spinach, yams, parsnips, carrots)	• Cold slices of skinless chicken breast or lean beef
• Nuts and seeds (almonds, walnuts, macadamia nuts, pecans, cashews, pistachios, hazelnuts, pine nuts, chestnuts, brazil nuts, pumpkin seeds, sunflower seeds)	• Sandwiches on gluten-free bread or a gluten-free wrap	• Salad	• Nuts or seeds
		• Rice pasta with tomato sauce	• Dried fruit
		• Stir Fry with rice or rice noodles	• Trail mix that includes a mixture of nuts, seeds and dried fruit
			• Beef or Turkey Jerky

WEEKLY MEAL PLAN EXAMPLE

One of our main goals with creating this cook book is to show you that eating healthy does not have to feel restrictive. Here is an example of what a weekly Best Bet Diet meal plan would look like. Once you get familiar and comfortable with the many recipes in this book, you can change up your meal plans so you are eating delicious and nutritious meals every day while feeling great!

After browsing through the recipes in this book, go ahead and create a few meal plans of your own. Repeating these plans weekly for a few months will create habits and hopefully get you well on your way to better health.

	MON	TUES	WED	THURS	FRI	SAT	SUN
BREAKFAST	• smoothie • smoked salmon or left over protein from dinner night before • tea, coffee or water	• bowl of fresh berries (blueberries, raspberries, strawberries) • leftover protein from dinner night before • tea, coffee or water	• trail mix with a mixture of nuts, seeds and dried fruit • banana or orange • tea, coffee or water	• bowl of blueberries, prunes • toasted rice bread or rice crackers with almond or cashew butter • tea, coffee or water	• smoothie • toasted rice bread with avocado • tea, coffee or water	• gluten-free chicken or beef sausages • eggs (if tolerated) • fruit • tea, coffee or water	• gluten-free waffles • bacon • fruit • tea, coffee or water
LUNCH	• leftover roast or chicken dinner • fresh vegetables or salad • fruit and nuts	• broccoli and tomato soup (page 78) • fruit	• leftover salad rolls • fruit	• leftover stir fry • fruit	• salad with lots of leafy greens and vegetables * option to add protein (canned salmon, tuna, leftover fish or chicken) • fruit	• tuna or chicken sandwich on a gluten-free bun or gluten-free wrap • fresh vegetables • fruit	• roasted chicken (store bought) • fresh vegetables or salad • fruit
DINNER	• maple salmon (page 117) * make extra salmon to have at breakfast the next day) • roasted vegetables • roasted potatoes • fruit	• salad rolls with chicken or shrimp (page 167) * make extra for lunch the next day) • fruit	• vegetable stir-fry with chicken or shrimp (page 169) * make extra for lunch the next day • fruit	• garlic lemon pickerel (page 114) * make extra fish for lunch the next day • roasted vegetables • basic greens salad (page 88) • fruit	• dine out (e.g. chicken curry and rice at a Thai restaurant)	• vegetable soup in Instant Pot (page 197) • add chicken to soup if you want a protein • basic greens salad (page 88) • fruit	• beef roast or oven roasted chicken * make extra for breakfast and lunches throughout the week • roasted potatoes • asparagus or other vegetable • salad • apple crumble (page 234)

* Remember to include snacks between meals such as fresh fruit, vegetables, trail mix (nuts, seeds, dried fruit), gluten-free crackers or jerky between meals. This will keep your energy up, increase nutrients and prevent you from craving foods you have eliminated.

SHOPPING LIST EXAMPLE

Meat
- ☐ chicken breast
- ☐ store-bought roasted chicken
- ☐ gluten, dairy and nitrate free chicken, turkey or beef sausages
- ☐ bacon (low salt)
- ☐ beef or lamb roast

Fish
- ☐ pickerel
- ☐ smoked salmon
- ☐ shrimp

Vegetables
- ☐ asparagus
- ☐ avocados
- ☐ broccoli
- ☐ cabbage
- ☐ carrots
- ☐ cauliflower
- ☐ celery
- ☐ cucumber
- ☐ romaine lettuce
- ☐ mushrooms
- ☐ green onion
- ☐ kale
- ☐ onions
- ☐ potatoes
- ☐ radishes
- ☐ red peppers
- ☐ spinach
- ☐ cherry tomatoes
- ☐ zucchini

Fruit
- ☐ apples (granny smith)
- ☐ bananas
- ☐ blueberries
- ☐ lemons
- ☐ oranges
- ☐ prunes
- ☐ raspberries
- ☐ strawberries

Grains
- ☐ rice bread
- ☐ rice wraps
- ☐ rice vermicelli

Liquids
- ☐ unsweetened almond milk, coconut milk (for smoothies)
- ☐ non-dairy creamer (coconut, almond milk creamers no soy)
- ☐ lemon juice

Oils and Condiments
- ☐ balsamic vinegar
- ☐ extra virgin olive oil
- ☐ dairy-free margarine
- ☐ coconut aminos (substitute for soy sauce)
- ☐ coconut oil
- ☐ sesame oil
- ☐ sweet chili sauce

Frozen food
- ☐ gluten and dairy free waffles

Canned or Boxed Items
- ☐ low sodium beef, chicken and vegetable broth
- ☐ canned diced tomatoes
- ☐ canned salmon
- ☐ canned tuna

Spices
- ☐ bay leaf
- ☐ gluten-free chicken, beef, vegetable bouillon cubes
- ☐ cinnamon
- ☐ ginger
- ☐ Italian seasoning
- ☐ nutmeg
- ☐ paprika
- ☐ black pepper
- ☐ cayenne pepper
- ☐ salt (half salt or salt free)
- ☐ turmeric
- ☐ fresh garlic
- ☐ ginger root

Baking
- ☐ brown sugar
- ☐ all purpose gluten-free flour mix (avoid corn flour in mix)

Snacking
- ☐ almonds
- ☐ cashews
- ☐ walnuts
- ☐ pecans
- ☐ sunflower seeds
- ☐ pumpkin seeds

Other
- ☐ coffee
- ☐ tea
- ☐ stevia
- ☐ almond butter
- ☐ cashew butter
- ☐ eggs (if tolerated)
- ☐ maple syrup
- ☐ red or white wine (in moderation)

PANTRY ITEMS

Here are a list of grocery items that are used in many of the recipes in this book and therefore it's helpful to always be stocked up on in your pantry.

☐ Extra virgin olive oil

☐ Avocado oil

☐ Cooking spray

☐ Margarine (dairy-free)

☐ Mayonnaise (egg and dairy-free)

☐ All-purpose gluten-free flour mix (avoid corn flour in mix) used to thicken sauces and gravy.

☐ Gluten-free Panko "breadcrumbs"

☐ Loaf of frozen rice flour bread

☐ Coconut aminos (organic coconut sauce) (soy sauce substitute used to make sauces for stir fry)

☐ Beef, chicken and vegetable broth (low salt or no salt)

☐ Gluten-free chicken, beef or vegetable bouillon cubes

☐ Rice noodles (spaghetti, fettuccine, vermicelli made from brown or white rice)

☐ Rice (white and brown)

☐ Rice milk, unsweetened almond milk or coconut milk

☐ Almond and cashew butter

☐ Unsalted almonds and cashews

☐ Banana chips

☐ Stevia

☐ Honey

☐ Balsamic and Apple cider vinegar

☐ Half salt or salt free (both reduce sodium intake)

☐ Spices: salt, course black pepper, lemon pepper, pepper flakes, chili powder, ground coriander, cumin, curry powder, dry mustard powder, garam masala, oregano, sage, thyme, turmeric

Going out for meals

Many people when starting this diet are concerned about how they will manage going out socially on a diet that restricts many common foods. Luckily this can be managed with some simple strategies.

FAMILY AND FRIENDS GATHERINGS

- Call ahead and explain your diet restrictions and ask what they are planning to serve.

- Bring a dish that you can share with the group that is Best Bet friendly (casserole, vegetable or fruit plate, side dish etc.).

- If the meal is going to be more challenging to work around, eat before so you are not hungry, and you can nibble at some of the available foods that are diet friendly.

TRAVELLING

- Rent accommodations that have cooking facilities that are helpful for cooking breakfasts, snacks, some dinners and storing BBD friendly foods.

- Restaurants can be an option with some planning. See below for dining out at restaurants.

- Supermarkets and health food stores now have many prepared foods that are acceptable (rotisserie chicken, salads, fruit and vegetable plates).

DINING OUT AT RESTAURANTS

- Again, share with friends and family your diet restrictions and try to find a restaurant which offers options on their menu that are Best Bet Diet friendly. Most restaurants have their menu online so it is easy to check in advance for Best Bet options.

- Openly discuss your food sensitivities with restaurant staff to ensure that they are aware of your issues so they can share them with the person cooking your meal.

- Restaurant staff are very accommodating. If you choose a menu item that has cheese or gluten products (like croutons) in it, you can ask them to exclude them from that menu item.

- Many restaurants have gluten-free options on their menu making it easier to work around the diet.

- Look for the salad section of the menu then customize your salad by asking for no cheese, croutons, etc. Also ask for a salad dressing that is Best Bet friendly like balsamic or just oil and vinegar. Most restaurants will on request add a chicken breast, shrimp or salmon to your salad for extra protein.

There is now such a variety of restaurants that can offer foods that are Best Bet friendly. Here is a chart showing different cuisines and examples of safe dishes you can order and what to avoid.

	WHAT TO ORDER	WHAT TO AVOID
JAPANESE	✓ sushi, sashimi, seaweed salad, avocado roll	✗ tempura, edamame (legumes), cream cheese rolls, miso soup (legumes), soy sauce
THAI	✓ most curries are safe as they use coconut milk (confirm with server), salad rolls, rice noodle dishes	✗ spring rolls, peanuts, MSG
VIETNAMESE	✓ salad rolls, Pho, Bun (no spring rolls), chicken skewers	✗ spring rolls, peanuts, MSG
MEXICAN	✓ taco salad (no cheese), guacamole, corn tortillas or better yet ask for lettuce wraps, rice and meat dishes	✗ flour tortillas, dishes with cheese
ITALIAN	✓ tomato-based sauces with gluten-free noodles (in moderation), chicken or veal with potatoes and vegetables as sides, gluten-free soups	✗ bread (many restaurants offer a gluten-free bread option), cream sauces, dishes with cheese
CHINESE	✓ beef and broccoli, fried rice, steamed vegetables	✗ soy can be a problem in Chinese cooking so discuss this with server, meat coated in batter, dumplings, MSG
INDIAN	✓ basmati rice, chicken dishes (without creamy sauces), rice biryani, salads, dairy-free vegetarian dishes	✗ samosa, naan, creamy dairy-based sauces
FAST FOOD	✓ most now have salad choices on the menu that you can adapt to the diet, grilled chicken (no bun), real fruit smoothies, rice or salad bowls	✗ red meat, deep fried food
BREAKFAST/ BRUNCH	✓ dairy-free smoothies, fruit, salad with or without protein, smoked salmon, eggs (if tolerated), substitute spinach or gluten-free hashbrowns or potato wedges in place of english muffins or toast	✗ cereal, yogurt, muffins, pancakes (they may have gluten-free options but ensure they are dairy-free as well)

BREAKFAST

Apple Kale Blueberry Smoothie

1–2 cups kale, fresh or frozen

½ green apple, chopped

1 cup coconut water

1 cup blueberries

1 tablespoon fresh grated ginger

1 teaspoon turmeric

pinch black pepper

½ cup coconut milk (optional)

1. Blend all ingredients together in blender.

Cherry Almond Smoothie

1 cup unsweetened almond milk

1 cup frozen cherries

½ banana

1–2 cups spinach

1 teaspoon chia or hemp hearts

1. Blend all ingredients together in blender.

Chocolate Mint Smoothie

1 cup unsweetened almond milk

1 tablespoon nut butter (almond, cashew)

1 banana

1 cup spinach

1 teaspoon cocoa powder

1 drop peppermint oil

1. Blend all ingredients together in blender.

Tahini Turmeric Smoothie

1 cup water (or almond milk or coconut milk)

2 cups greens (romaine, red/green leaf, chard, beet greens)

½ banana (frozen or fresh)

1 cup frozen fruit (mango, strawberry, blueberry)

1 tablespoon pumpkin seeds (or tahini butter)

1 teaspoon turmeric

1 teaspoon fresh grated ginger (optional)

1. Blend all ingredients together in blender.

Power Trail Mix

2 cups almonds

2 cups walnuts

2 cups pecans

1 cup sunflower seeds

1 cup pumpkin seeds

½ cup raisins

½ cup dried cranberries

1. Mix all ingredients together and put them in a container.

TIPS
- Take to the office and on holidays for a convenient snack.

- Any of your favourite nuts, seeds and dried fruit can be used.

Carrot Ginger Soup (page 70)

SOUP

Carrot Ginger Soup

SERVES 4–6

2 tablespoons olive oil

2 medium onions, chopped

3 tablespoons fresh ginger, minced or grated

4 cups carrots, chopped

1 potato, cut in chunks

6 cups vegetable broth

salt and pepper to taste

¼ teaspoon nutmeg

cilantro, parsley, lemon peel or green onion for garnish (optional)

1. Sauté onions and ginger in olive oil for 4–5 minutes or until onion is softened in soup pot.

2. Add carrots, potatoes, vegetable broth to onion mixture then cover and simmer for 30–40 minutes until vegetables are soft.

3. Pour mixture into blender and blend completely.

4. Add salt and pepper to taste.

5. Add nutmeg.

6. Serve garnished with cilantro, parsley, lemon peel or chopped green onion.

Homemade Chicken Stock Recipe

MAKES 12 CUPS

1 (4 to 5 pound) whole chicken or
  equal amounts of bone-in, skin-on chicken
  pieces

1 medium yellow onion, quartered

1 clove garlic, quartered

2 celery ribs, cut into large pieces

2 carrots, cut into large pieces

1 teaspoon salt

1 teaspoon freshly ground black pepper

1 teaspoon thyme

8–10 cups water

STOVE
1. Place chicken in large stockpot.

2. Add onion, garlic, celery, carrots, salt, pepper, thyme and cover with 10–12 cups cold water.

3. Cook on low simmer, covered for 4 hours.

4. Add more water if needed to keep chicken covered with water while cooking.

5. Remove chicken from stock and refrigerate for future recipes.

6. Strain vegetables from stock and discard.

SLOW COOKER
1. Place chicken in 6-quart slow cooker.

2. Add onion, garlic, celery, carrots, salt, pepper, thyme and cover with 8–10 cups cold water.

3. Cover and cook 4 hours on high or 8 hours on low.

4. Remove chicken from stock and use for other recipes. Strain vegetables from stock and discard.

INSTANT POT
1. Place chicken in Instant Pot.

2. Add onion, garlic, celery, carrots, salt, pepper, thyme and cover.

3. Add fresh, cold water to the 10 cup line on the inside of the interior pot of the Instant Pot. Cook 25 minutes at high pressure. Let pressure release naturally.

4. Remove chicken from stock. Strain vegetables from stock and discard.

5. Allow stock to cool, and store in freezer-safe, airtight containers. Refrigerate or freeze until ready to use. Stock will keep in the refrigerator for up to a week and in the freezer for 3 months up to 1 year.

Sweet Potato, Ginger & Tomato Soup

SERVES 4

3 tablespoons olive oil

2 medium onions, finely sliced

2 large sweet potatoes, peeled and diced

1 tablespoon ginger root, peeled and chopped

2 (16 oz) cans chopped tomatoes

2 cups low salt vegetable or chicken broth

salt and freshly ground black pepper

1. Heat the oil in a wide pan; add the onions, sweet potato and ginger root.

2. Cover the pan and simmer for 15–20 minutes or until the vegetables are quite soft.

3. Add the tomatoes and broth.

4. Bring to a boil and simmer for 30–40 minutes.

5. Then puree in a food processor.

6. Season to taste with salt and pepper, if needed.

7. Serve either hot or cold.

Cabbage Roll Soup

SERVES 6

1 large onion

3 cloves garlic, minced

1 pound lean ground beef

½ pound lean ground pork

¾ cup uncooked long grain rice

1 medium head cabbage

1 (28 oz) can diced tomatoes

2 tablespoons tomato paste

4 cups beef broth

1½ cups V8 (or other vegetable juice)

1 teaspoon paprika

1 teaspoon thyme

1 tablespoon Worcestershire sauce
(French's is gluten-free)

1 bay leaf

salt and pepper

1. In a large pot, brown onion, garlic, pork and beef. Drain any fat.

2. Stir in chopped cabbage and let cook until slightly softened (about 3 minutes).

3. Add all remaining ingredients, bring to a boil and reduce heat to medium low.

4. Cover and simmer on low until rice is fully cooked (about 25–30 minutes).

5. Remove bay leaf and serve.

Savory Carrot Soup

SERVES 4

1 tablespoon extra virgin olive oil

1 pound carrots cut into small pieces

1 large potato, cubed

1 medium onion, chopped

1 teaspoon tarragon

3 cups low salt vegetable broth

½ cup orange juice

salt

chopped fresh parsley or scallions
to garnish

1. Heat the oil in large saucepan over medium heat.

2. Add carrots, potato, onion and tarragon.

3. Toss and cook for about 5 minutes (till soft not brown).

4. Add the vegetable broth.

5. Lower the heat and simmer for about 30 minutes until the vegetables are tender.

6. Allow to cool and then pureeing in a blender or food processor.

7. Then add the orange juice, salt to taste, and garnish.

8. Serve either heated or chilled.

VARIATION
This soup can be made with pumpkin or sweet potato, adding pumpkin pie spices, for Thanksgiving.

Asparagus Celery Soup

SERVES 4

1 tablespoon coconut oil

1 tablespoon extra virgin olive oil

1 small leek, thinly sliced

2 celery stalks, chopped

2 medium garlic cloves, minced

1 small white potato, chopped small

4–5 cups low-sodium vegetable broth

1 pound asparagus, chopped

⅛ teaspoon pepper

⅛ teaspoon ground nutmeg

¼ cup fresh basil leaves

chives (optional)

1. Melt coconut oil and olive oil in a large pot over medium heat and cook leek and celery until tender, 2–3 minutes.

2. Stir in garlic and cook for 1 minute.

3. Add potato and 3 cups broth, bring to a boil, reduce heat to medium, cover and cook for 10 minutes, or until potato pieces are tender.

4. Add asparagus and cook for 3–4 minutes more, or until tender.

5. Stir in pepper and nutmeg.

6. Transfer soup to food processor, add basil, and puree (in batches if necessary) adding remaining 1–2 cups broth as needed to adjust consistency.

7. Season to taste with salt and pepper.

8. Serve hot, sprinkle with chives if desired.

Cauliflower Soup

SERVES 2

2 tablespoons olive oil

1 large onion, peeled and chopped

2 garlic cloves, chopped

1 potato, chopped

1 large cauliflower, cut into florets

1¼ cups chicken broth

1¼ cups original rice dream

1 pinch nutmeg

salt and pepper

1 tablespoon chopped parsley for garnish

1. Using a deep saucepan, heat 2 tablespoons olive oil, add chopped onion, cook until soft but not brown, about 5 minutes.

2. Add chopped garlic cloves.

3. Place cauliflower and chopped potato into saucepan, followed by chicken broth and rice dream and bring to boil.

4. Cover the soup and simmer for 15–20 minutes or until cauliflower is soft.

5. Puree the mixture and add nutmeg.

6. Season to taste with salt and pepper and add a sprinkling of chopped parsley.

Broccoli & Tomato Soup

SERVES 2

1 large head of broccoli, trimmed and cut into florets

1 onion, peeled and chopped

1 clove garlic, peeled and chopped

1½ cups tomatoes, diced

1 cup vegetable broth

1 tablespoon coconut oil (or oil of your choice)

3 pieces of cooked bacon

1. Heat the oil in a large saucepan.

2. Add the onion and garlic and sauté gently for 3 minutes.

3. Add the broccoli and cook for a further 2 minutes.

4. Add the tomatoes and broth, bring to a boil, cover and cook for 15 minutes until the broccoli is tender.

5. Blend with either a hand blender or food processor.

6. Season to taste.

7. Pan fry bacon till crisp and add to top off soup before serving.

Spinach & Orange Soup

SERVES 2

1 tablespoon olive oil

1 tablespoon rice flour

1 onion, finely chopped

1 (8 oz) package of spinach, washed and shredded

1½ cups of chicken broth

2 oranges segmented

¼ teaspoon of nutmeg

salt and freshly ground pepper

1. Fry onion in olive oil until soft, stir in the flour, cook 1–2 minutes.

2. Add the broth a little at a time and bring to boil.

3. Stir in the spinach, orange segments, nutmeg and seasoning.

4. Pour into blender and blend for 1 minute until soft.

5. Adjust seasoning and serve.

Shrimp, Scallops & Crabmeat Chowder

SERVES 6

2 cups water

1 teaspoon salt (optional)

¼ pound shrimp

¼ pound scallops

1 can crabmeat (120 grams)

2½ cups tomato juice

1 medium onion, chopped finely

3 medium potatoes, peeled and cut into 1 inch cubes

2 large celery stalks, diced

2 large carrots, diced

1 tablespoon fresh parsley, chopped

freshly ground pepper to taste

pinch cayenne pepper

1–2 tablespoons rice flour (or arrowroot flour) to thicken

1. In large saucepan, bring 2 cups of water and 1 teaspoon of salt to a boil.

2. Add shrimp and scallops and cook for 5 minutes.

3. Remove shrimp and scallops, saving water.

4. Set shrimp and scallops aside to cool slightly.

5. Add tomato juice, onions, potatoes, celery, carrots, parsley, salt and pepper, and cayenne to water in saucepan.

6. Cover and simmer gently for 5 minutes.

7. Add shrimp and scallops and crabmeat and simmer 2–3 minutes.

8. Stir rice flour or arrowroot flour into a small amount of cold tomato juice until thoroughly blended and then add mixture to soup to thicken.

9. Cook, stirring over medium heat for 5 minutes, then serve (do not bring to boil).

Broccoli Mandarin Salad (page 85)

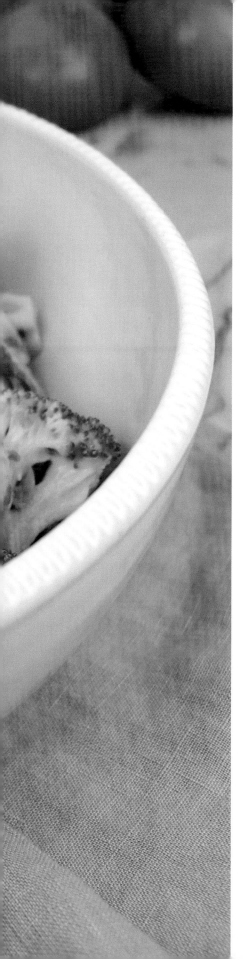

SALAD

Salad Dressings

DRESSING FOR FRUIT SALAD

2 tablespoons orange juice

2 tablespoons lime juice

2 teaspoons honey

¼ teaspoon hot pepper flakes

½ cup canola oil or extra virgin olive oil

1. Whisk together orange juice, lime juice, honey, pepper flakes and oil.

COLORADO SPINACH SALAD DRESSING

⅓ cup orange juice

⅓ cup lemon juice

fresh ground pepper to taste

1 teaspoon tarragon, minced

⅔ cup extra virgin olive oil

1. Combine orange juice and lemon juice and mix well.

2. Add pepper, tarragon and stir.

3. Pour mixture into a large plastic container, add the oil, and shake vigorously to blend. Makes 1 cup.

TOMATO DRESSING

1 cup fresh tomatoes

½ cup extra virgin olive oil

⅓ cup lemon juice

1 garlic clove

1 onion chopped

1. Put all ingredients in a blender and blend until smooth. Makes 1½ cups.

Broccoli Mandarin Salad

SERVES 6

4 cups fresh broccoli florets

½ cup raisins

8 slices bacon, cooked and chopped

2 cups fresh mushrooms, sliced

½ cup slivered toasted almonds

1 (10 oz) can mandarin oranges, drained
(or 3–4 fresh mandarin oranges)

½ red onion, sliced

DRESSING

2 eggs

½ cup sugar

1 tablespoon rice flour for thickening

1 teaspoon dry mustard

¼ cup white wine vinegar

¼ cup water

½ cup mayonnaise

1. In saucepan, whisk together eggs, sugar, flour and dry mustard.

2. Add vinegar and water and cook on medium–low heat until thickened. Stir continuously.

3. Remove from heat and stir in mayonnaise. Let cool.

4. Mix broccoli and dressing and marinate for several hours in fridge. Add remaining ingredients and toss well.

Fresh Spinach Salad

SERVES 4–6

8 cups crisp spinach, stems removed
and broken up in bite sized pieces

8 slices bacon, cooked and crumbled

4 green onions, finely chopped

2 cups fresh mushrooms, sliced

2 cups fresh cauliflower, sliced

TANGY DRESSING

1 garlic clove, minced

2 tablespoons cider or red wine vinegar

1 teaspoon sugar

½ teaspoon salt

1 teaspoon dry mustard

½ teaspoon freshly ground pepper

¼ cup extra virgin olive oil

1. In a small bowl, beat all dressing ingredients together and refrigerate.

2. Combine salad ingredients in a large bowl.

3. Toss with dressing just before serving.

Basic Greens Salad

SERVES 4

salad greens (lettuce, kale, spinach)

1 cucumber, chopped

1 carrot, chopped

2 green onions, chopped

1 red pepper, sliced

4 radishes, sliced

cherry tomatoes

1 avocado, sliced

DRESSING

extra virgin olive oil

balsamic vinegar

1. Mix the salad ingredients and sprinkle with oil and vinegar to taste.

TIPS

- Easy to make a large batch and take all week for lunches.

- Dressing can be made separate and avocado can be added right before serving.

Shrimp Stuffed Avocados

SERVES 4

4 large avocados, peeled and halved, seeds removed

1½ cups small salad shrimp, cooked and washed

1 tablespoon lemon juice

1 tablespoon onion powder

1 teaspoon black pepper

1 tablespoon paprika

1. Set avocados on serving plate with cut side facing up.

2. Combine shrimp, lemon juice, onion powder, and pepper in medium-sized mixing bowl.

3. Spoon shrimp mixture onto each avocado, covering generously.

4. Sprinkle top of each stuffed avocado with paprika before serving.

Avocado Fruit Salad

SERVES 4

1 avocado

2 tablespoons lime juice

1 papaya

2 oranges

1 grapefruit

1 red onion

1 head of romaine lettuce

DRESSING

2 tablespoons orange juice

2 tablespoons lime juice

2 teaspoons honey

¼ teaspoon hot pepper flakes

½ cup canola oil or extra virgin olive oil

1. Whisk together orange juice, lime juice, honey, pepper flakes and oil.

2. Peel and slice avocado.

3. Sprinkle with 1 tablespoon lime juice.

4. Peel, seed and slice papaya thinly.

5. Peel oranges and grapefruit. Cut fruit into segments.

6. Chop red onion.

7. In a large bowl combine avocado, papaya, orange and grapefruit segments and onion. Set aside.

8. Before serving, pour dressing over fruit and toss well.

9. Spoon onto lettuce lined platter.

TIP

Great with chicken or as a luncheon salad.

Caesar Salad

SERVES 4–6

1–2 romaine hearts, broken up
into bite size pieces

CAESAR SALAD DRESSING

1 clove garlic, minced

½ cup extra virgin olive oil

½ teaspoon salt

¼ teaspoon freshly ground pepper

¼ teaspoon dry mustard

1½ teaspoons Worcestershire sauce
(French's is gluten-free)

3 anchovies, drained and chopped

juice of ½ lemon (2 tablespoons)

GLUTEN-FREE CROUTONS

3–4 slices of rice bread or
acceptable alternative

1–2 cloves of garlic, minced

2 tablespoons extra virgin olive oil

DRESSING

1. In jar add all the dressing ingredients
   and shake vigorously.

2. Refrigerate for an hour before serving
   so flavours can mix.

3. Mix lettuce with dressing and sprinkle
   on croutons.

CROUTONS

1. Toast the slices of rice bread.

2. Cut up toasted bread slices into
   small cubes.

3. Heat oil in non-stick fry pan and
   add garlic.

4. Toss in croutons and stir lightly till
   croutons are covered evenly in oil
   mixture. Serve when warm.

Honey Lemon Kale Salad

SERVES 4

8 cups loosely packed kale, well rinsed

1 cup dried cranberries

1 small red onion, thinly sliced

1 crisp apple

1 ripe firm pear

1 cup pecans, toasted on a dry skillet

HONEY LEMON DRESSING

4 tablespoons fresh lemon juice

2 tablespoons extra virgin olive oil

1 tablespoon honey

½ teaspoon salt

⅛ teaspoon black pepper

1. Combine all dressing ingredients and stir together until honey dissolves. Set aside.

2. Rinse and strip kale leaves. Chop in bite-sized pieces. Rinse the chopped leaves a second time to ensure there isn't any dust hidden in the curly leaves then dry in a salad spinner.

3. Place kale in a salad bowl, top with 1 cup cranberries and drizzle with dressing. Stir well, cover and refrigerate 4 hours or overnight.

4. Before serving, add sliced apples, sliced pears, thinly sliced onions and toasted pecans. Toss to combine.

TIP

Add grilled or roasted chicken for a protein.

Almond Chicken Salad

SERVES 2

1 cup chicken breast, diced

1 cup romaine lettuce, chopped

1 cup butter lettuce, shredded

¼ cup red cabbage

½ cup almonds, sliced

¼ cup chopped dates

1–2 tablespoons extra-virgin olive oil

1–2 tablespoons freshly squeezed orange juice

1. Combine all ingredients except liquids in a large serving bowl.

2. Toss with oil and freshly squeezed orange juice.

Fruit & Lime Chicken Salad

SERVES 6

3 tablespoons sugar

¼ cup vinegar (lemon juice)

2 tablespoons lime juice

dash of salt

¼ teaspoon poppy seeds

½ cup canola oil (or extra virgin oil)

3 cups of cubed cooked chicken breast

1 honeydew melon

1 cantaloupe

1 romaine lettuce

½ cup strawberries

½ cup green grapes

½ cup pecan halves, toasted

½ cup blueberries

1. Combine sugar, vinegar, lime juice, mustard, salt and poppy seeds in a blender. Blend to mix.

2. Gradually add oil in a thin stream.

3. Cover and blend 2 minutes until dressing is slightly thickened.

4. Reserve ⅓ cup and pour remaining dressing over chicken. Chill.

5. To serve, line 4–6 salad plates with lettuce and arrange honeydew and cantaloupe wedges around edge.

6. Spoon chicken into center.

7. Toss strawberries, pecans and blueberries in reserved dressing.

8. Spoon over.

Mandarin Avocado Salad

SERVES 4

1 head butter lettuce or romaine

1 (10 oz/284 ml) can mandarin orange sections, drained (or two mandarin oranges, peeled)

1 medium avocado

1 medium red onion, sliced thin

ITALIAN DRESSING

½ cup mayonnaise

1 teaspoon dry mustard

1 tablespoon vinegar

2 tablespoons olive oil

½ teaspoon oregano

½ teaspoon basil

(1 teaspoon Italian seasoning can be used in place of oregano and basil)

1. Tear lettuce into bite-size pieces in salad bowl.

2. Add orange sections, slices of avocado and thin slices of red onion.

3. In a small bowl, combine all Italian dressing ingredients and mix well.

4. Toss salad with dressing and serve.

Waldorf Salad

SERVES 2

2 cups un-peeled red apples, diced

2 tablespoons lemon juice

2 tablespoon extra virgin olive oil (or flaxseed oil)

1 cup celery, thinly sliced

½ cup chopped walnuts

½ cup raisins

2 cups iceberg lettuce leaves

1. Toss together first 6 ingredients.

2. Serve on top of lettuce bed.

Lemon Dijon Garden Pasta Salad

SERVES 6–8

6 cups cooked cold pasta (rice pasta)

½ cup red pepper, chopped

½ cup cucumber, chopped

½ cup red onion, sliced

½ cup yellow cherry tomatoes

½ cup red cherry tomatoes

½ cup kalamata olives

⅓ cup chopped fresh herbs (mint, basil, oregano and chives)

¼ cup sweet pickle relish

LEMON DIJON DRESSING

½ cup mayonnaise

¼ cup lemon juice (or apple cider vinegar)

zest of 1 lemon

salt and pepper to season

3 tablespoons whole grain Dijon mustard

1 tablespoon sugar

1. Whisk or shake all dressing ingredients together and set aside.

2. Combine all the salad ingredients.

3. Mix with Lemon Dijon Dressing.

FISH

Fish Marinades

SEAFOOD HERB-WINE MARINADE

1 cup dry white wine

¼ cup lemon juice

2 cloves of garlic, minced or pressed

1 teaspoon dry rosemary

2 tablespoons extra virgin olive oil

1. In a small pan, combine wine, lemon juice, garlic cloves, rosemary and oil.

2. Heat to simmering, remove from heat, cover and let stand for an hour.

3. Pour over fish; cover and refrigerate for 30–60 minutes.

ITALIAN-STYLE MARINADE

¾ cup extra virgin olive oil

¼ cup lemon juice

1 clove garlic, minced or pressed

½ teaspoon oregano leaves

1. Combine oil, lemon juice, garlic and oregano leaves.

2. Pour over fish, cover and refrigerate for 30 minutes to two hours.

LEMON-ONION BASTE

½ cup lemon juice

¼ cup extra virgin olive oil

¼ teaspoon each salt and sugar

dash of pepper

¼ cup green onion, chopped

1. Combine lemon juice, oil, salt, sugar, pepper and green onion.

2. Use to baste frequently during cooking.

DRY RUB FOR SALMON

4 tablespoons sugar

1 tablespoon chili powder

1 teaspoon pepper

½ tablespoon cumin

½ tablespoon paprika

½ teaspoon salt

¼ teaspoon dry mustard

¼ teaspoon cinnamon

1. Mix all ingredients and rub on salmon.

LEMON DILL MARINADE

⅓ cup extra virgin olive oil

1 teaspoon lemon rind

¼ cup lemon juice

2 tablespoons chopped fresh dill
(or 2 teaspoons dried dill)

¼ teaspoon each salt and pepper

1. Whisk together oil, lemon rind, lemon juice, salt and pepper.

2. Pour over fish and marinate for 30 minutes and use to baste while fish is cooking.

LIME CUMIN MARINADE

¼ cup extra virgin olive oil

¼ cup lime juice

4 teaspoons Worcestershire sauce
(French's is gluten-free)

1½ teaspoons ground cumin

1 teaspoon lime rind, grated

2 cloves of garlic, minced

¼ teaspoon each salt and pepper

1. Whisk together oil, lime juice, Worcestershire sauce, cumin, lime rind, garlic, salt and pepper.

2. Pour over fish and marinate for 30 minutes and use to baste while fish is cooking.

KONA LOCAL MARINADE

½ cup unsweetened pineapple juice

¼ cup extra virgin olive oil

3 tablespoons lime juice

2 tablespoons fresh ginger-root,
finely grated

1. Combine all ingredients in a small bowl and whisk until well blended. Use to marinate fish, beef and chicken when barbecuing. Makes about one cup.

TARTAR SAUCE

3 tablespoons mayonnaise

1 teaspoon lemon juice

4 dill pickles, finely diced

1 tablespoon dill (fresh or dried)

1. Combine all ingredients in a small bowl and whisk until well blended. Serve on the side.

Speedy Lemon Baked Fish

SERVES 4

½ teaspoon grated lemon rind

1 tablespoon lemon juice

1 tablespoon extra virgin olive oil

2 cloves garlic, minced

1 pound fish fillets (sole or tilapia)

salt and pepper

1. Stir together lemon rind, juice, oil and garlic.

OVEN METHOD

1. Arrange fillets in shallow baking dish sprinkle with salt and pepper to taste.

2. Spread lemon mixture over fish. Bake in 450°F oven for 8 to 10 minutes or until fish is opaque and flakes easily when tested with fork.

MICROWAVE METHOD

1. Arrange fillets in round microwaveable dish with thickest part toward outside.

2. Sprinkle with salt and pepper to taste.

3. Spread lemon mixture over fish.

4. Cover with waxed paper; microwave at high for 4 to 6 minutes or until fish is opaque and flakes easily when tested with fork.

5. Let stand covered for 5 minutes.

Grilled Cod with Spicy Citrus Marinade

SERVES 2

¼ cup orange juice

1½ tablespoons lemon juice

3 tablespoons lime juice

⅛ teaspoon cayenne pepper

2 garlic cloves, minced

2 tablespoons extra virgin olive oil

⅓ cup water

1 pound cod fillets

2 tablespoons fresh chives, finely chopped

1 tablespoon fresh thyme, finely chopped

1. Combine orange, lemon, and lime juices in a bowl with cayenne pepper, garlic, olive oil, and water to make marinade.

2. Place fish in a flat dish.

3. Pour in all but ¼ cup of the marinade.

4. Let stand in refrigerator for 15 to 30 minutes.

5. Broil fish for 3–4 minutes per side, basting often with the marinade.

6. After removing fish from the broiler, pour on remaining marinade and sprinkle with chives and thyme.

Shrimp & Scallop Gluten-Free Linguine

SERVES 4

1 pound linguine (gluten-free)

12 jumbo shrimp, peeled and deveined

12 large sea scallops

freshly ground pepper

4 tablespoons oil mixture (half extra virgin olive oil and half butter substitute–Becel)

2 cloves garlic, minced

2 tablespoons fresh lemon juice, plus lemon wedges for garnish

½ cup dry white wine

¼ cup torn fresh basil

2 tablespoons fresh parsley, chopped

1. Bring a large pot of salted water to a boil.

2. Add the linguine and cook as the label directs.

3. Meanwhile, heat a large skillet over medium-high heat.

4. Pat the shrimp and scallops dry, then season with salt and pepper. Add 2 tablespoons of oil mixture (extra virgin olive oil and butter substitute) to the pan and cook the shrimp until golden on one side, about 3 minutes.

5. Turn the shrimp and add half of the garlic; cook until the garlic is fragrant but the shrimp are still translucent (1 to 2 more minutes). Transfer the shrimp to a plate.

6. Add the scallops to the skillet and cook until golden on one side, about 3 minutes. Turn the scallops, add the remaining garlic and cook 1 to 2 more minutes.

7. Add the lemon juice and wine and bring to a boil, scraping up any browned bits with a wooden spoon.

8. Cook until the sauce is reduced by half, about 3 minutes.

9. Return the shrimp to the pan, then add the basil and the remaining 2 tablespoons oil mixture. Season with salt and pepper.

10. Drain the pasta and transfer to a large serving bowl. Toss with the shrimp, scallops and sauce; garnish with parsley and lemon wedges.

Spicy Roasted Halibut

SERVES 4

1 tablespoon lime (or lemon juice)

2 teaspoons water

1½ teaspoons chili powder

1 teaspoon paprika

1 teaspoon pepper

1 teaspoon dried oregano

1 teaspoon dried thyme

¼ teaspoon garlic powder

¼ teaspoon salt

4 halibut (or swordfish or salmon steaks) (1½ pounds)

1. In small bowl, whisk together lime juice, water, chili powder, paprika, pepper, oregano, thyme, garlic powder and salt; rub gently onto both sides of fish.

2. Place fish on baking sheet. Bake at 425°F for about 10 minutes or until fish is opaque and flakes easily when tested with fork.

Tomato Basil Halibut

SERVES 6

2 tablespoons extra virgin olive oil

2 onions sliced

1½ cups of canned plum tomatoes (including juice)

½ teaspoon each salt and pepper

1½ pounds halibut steaks

1 tablespoon fresh basil, chopped

1. In heavy saucepan, over medium heat add onions to oil and cook for 10 minutes or until just beginning to brown.

2. Stir in tomatoes and juice, breaking up with fork.

3. Sprinkle with half of the salt and pepper.

4. Cook for about 3 minutes or until slightly thickened.

5. Cut halibut into 6 pieces, removing bones; sprinkle with remaining salt and pepper.

6. Place in greased 9 x 13 inch baking dish.

7. Spoon tomato sauce over fish; sprinkle with basil.

8. Bake at 450°F for 10 to 15 minutes or until fish is opaque and flakes easily when tested with fork.

Poached Salmon in Tomato Broth

SERVES 4–6

2 cups canned tomatoes

¼ cup white wine (or chicken broth)

2 teaspoons extra virgin olive oil

1 teaspoon fennel seeds

4–6 salmon fillets or steaks (about 4 oz)

½ cup chopped fresh basil

salt and pepper to taste

1. Puree the tomatoes in a blender or food processor.

2. Combine the pureed tomatoes, wine or broth, olive oil, and fennel seeds in a large skillet over moderate heat.

3. Place salmon fillets in sauce.

4. Sprinkle with chopped basil and season with salt and pepper.

5. Simmer covered for 10 minutes.

Honey Ginger Mahi Mahi

SERVES 4

2 tablespoons honey

3 tablespoons coconut aminos (soy sauce substitute)

3 tablespoons balsamic vinegar

1 teaspoon fresh ginger root, grated

1 clove garlic, crushed

2 teaspoons olive oil

4 (6 oz) mahi mahi fillets

salt and pepper to taste

1 tablespoon vegetable oil

1. In a shallow glass dish, stir together the honey, coconut aminos, balsamic vinegar, ginger, garlic and olive oil.

2. Season fish fillets with salt and pepper and place them into the dish.

3. If the fillets have skin on them, place them skin side down.

4. Cover, and refrigerate for 20 minutes to marinate.

5. Heat vegetable oil in a large skillet over medium-high heat.

6. Remove fish from the dish and reserve marinade.

7. Fry fish for 4 to 6 minutes on each side, turning only once, until fish flakes easily with a fork. Remove fillets to a serving platter and keep warm.

8. Pour reserved marinade into the skillet, and heat over medium heat until the mixture reduces to a glaze consistently. Spoon glaze over fish and serve immediately.

Grilled Salmon with Lemon Dill Marinade

SERVES 4

4 salmon steaks

LEMON DILL MARINADE

⅓ cup extra virgin olive oil

1 teaspoon lemon rind

¼ cup lemon juice

**2 tablespoons chopped fresh dill
(or 2 teaspoon dried dill)**

¼ teaspoon each salt and pepper

1. Whisk together oil, lemon rind and juice, dill, salt and pepper.

2. Pour into a shallow glass dish.

3. Add salmon steaks to marinade, turning to coat.

4. Cover and marinate for up to 30 minutes, turning occasionally.

5. Reserving marinade, place salmon on greased barbecue grill over medium-high heat.

6. Close lid and cook, turning halfway through, basting frequently and using all the marinade, for 10 minutes per inch of thickness or until fish is opaque and flakes easily when tested with fork.

Garlic Lemon Pickerel

SERVES 4

1 pound pickerel fillets

3 tablespoons olive oil

3 tablespoons lemon juice

2 cloves garlic, minced

½ teaspoon basil

1 green onion, sliced

salt and pepper to taste

1. In small bowl, stir together oil, lemon juice, garlic, basil and onion.

2. Place fillets in shallow baking dish and sprinkle with salt and pepper.

3. Spread oil and lemon mixture over the fish.

4. Bake fish in 450°F for about 10 minutes, or until fish is opaque.

Lemon Dill Cedar Plank Salmon

SERVES 4

4 fillets of salmon (or rainbow trout)

6 tablespoons olive oil

4 large cloves of garlic, chopped or crushed

¼ cup chopped fresh dill (or 1 tablespoon dried dill)

1 teaspoon lemon zest, grated

¼ teaspoon sea salt

1 teaspoon freshly ground pepper

8 lemon slices

1. Soak cedar plank in water for at least 30 minutes.

2. Mix together in a small bowl the olive oil, garlic, dill, lemon zest, salt and pepper.

3. Preheat BBQ to 500°F and then turn the burners on one half of the BBQ to the lowest setting.

4. Rub each fillet with the olive oil mixture and place them on the cedar plank.

5. Top each fillet with 2 slices of fresh lemon.

6. Put the cedar planked salmon on the low side of the BBQ and close the lid.

7. Cook the salmon for approximately 20–30 minutes until the thickest part of the fish is opaque (internal temperature of 130°F).

TIPS
- Also delicious served cold on top of a salad.

- Great for lunch the next day.

Salmon Steaks in Curry Sauce

SERVES 2

2 (8 oz) salmon steaks

2 teaspoons curry powder

1 teaspoon turmeric

½ teaspoon cayenne pepper

1 cup chicken broth (low salt)

4 teaspoons white wine

1. Wash salmon and place in shallow baking dish.

2. Mix curry, turmeric, and pepper with chicken broth and pour over fish.

3. Pour in white wine and cover with foil.

4. Bake at 350°F for 20 to 30 minutes. Salmon should flake easily with fork.

Maple Salmon

SERVES 4

4 salmon fillets

⅓ cup extra virgin olive oil

⅓ cup maple syrup

1. Heat oven to 400°F.

2. Mix oil and syrup.

3. Place salmon in greased oven safe dish.

4. Pour syrup mixture over salmon turning fish once to cover.

5. Bake for 30 minutes.

TIP
Line dish with parchment paper for easy clean-up.

Baked Salmon with Bacon-Avocado Salsa

SERVES 4

4 salmon fillets

1 teaspoon ground cumin

1 teaspoon paprika

1 teaspoon onion powder

½ teaspoon chili powder

2 tablespoons lemon juice

2 tablespoons olive oil

salt and freshly ground black pepper

BACON–AVOCADO SALSA

2 avocados, ripe, peeled and diced

1 plum tomato, seeded and chopped

½ red onion, minced

4 bacon strips, cooked and chopped

1 tablespoon fresh lime (or lemon juice)

½ teaspoon ground cumin

salt and freshly ground black pepper

1. Preheat oven to 400°F.

2. In a bowl, combine the cumin, paprika, onion powder, and chili powder; season to taste with salt and pepper.

3. Brush the salmon fillets with the olive oil and lemon juice.

4. Sprinkle the salmon fillets with the spice mixture and place in a baking dish.

5. Cook in the oven 12 to 15 minutes.

6. In a bowl, combine the ingredients for the Bacon-Avocado Salsa.

7. Season the salsa with salt and pepper to taste and gently toss until well mixed.

8. Serve the fish topped with the Bacon–Avocado Salsa.

Salmon Poached in Fennel

SERVES 4

1 tablespoon extra virgin olive oil

½ cup onion, chopped

½ cup carrot, chopped

½ cup fennel, chopped

4 garlic cloves, finely chopped

2 lemons cut into thin rounds

1 cup canned chopped tomatoes, drained

1 bay leaf

4 sprigs of fresh thyme (or
¼ teaspoon dried thyme leaves)

4 salmon steaks (12 oz each), cleaned and
ready to cook

3 sprigs of parsley

¼ teaspoon salt

¼ teaspoon freshly ground pepper

2 cups chicken broth

1 tablespoon parsley, chopped

1. Heat the olive oil in a large skillet.

2. Add the onion, carrot, fennel and garlic. Cover and cook over medium heat, stirring occasionally, until the vegetables are tender, 6 to 8 minutes.

3. Add the lemon slices, tomatoes, bay leaf, thyme and parsley sprigs.

4. Place the fish over the vegetables. Season with salt and pepper.

5. Pour the chicken broth over the fish.

6. Cover the skillet and bring the liquid to a boil.

7. Reduce the heat to low and simmer 10 to 15 minutes, or until the fish is firm to the touch and opaque.

8. Remove the fish to a serving plate and spoon the vegetables over the fish, using a slotted spoon. Boil down the liquid remaining in the skillet until 1 cup remains. Pour over the fish.

9. Garnish with the chopped parsley and chives before serving.

Seafood Thai Green Curry Gluten-Free Linguine

SERVES 4

2½ tablespoons vegetable oil

1 (4-inch-long) fresh hot red chili, thinly sliced crosswise

3 scallions, white and green parts thinly sliced separately

1 pound sea scallops

¾ pound large shrimp, shelled and deveined

1 (14 oz) can unsweetened coconut milk

1 tablespoon Thai green curry paste

¼ cup chicken broth (or water)

1 tablespoon packed light brown sugar

1½ tablespoons fish sauce

1 tablespoon fresh lime juice

12 oz dried thin linguine (gluten-free)

½ cup fresh cilantro, chopped

1. Heat 1 tablespoon oil in a 12-inch nonstick skillet over moderately high heat until hot but not smoking, then sauté chili and white parts of scallions, stirring occasionally, until lightly browned.

2. Transfer with a slotted spoon to paper towels to drain.

3. Pat scallops and shrimp, dry separately and season with salt.

4. Heat remaining 1½ tablespoons oil in same skillet over moderately high heat until hot but not smoking, then cook scallops until browned, 2 to 3 minutes on each side (scallops will be almost cooked through).

5. Transfer scallops to a bowl with slotted spoon and sauté shrimp in same skillet, stirring occasionally, until almost cooked through, about 3 minutes. Add shrimp to scallops.

6. Add coconut milk, curry paste, broth, brown sugar, fish sauce and lime juice to skillet, then simmer, stirring occasionally, 5 minutes.

7. Meanwhile, cook linguine in a 6 to 8-quart pot of boiling salted water until al dente, then drain in a colander.

8. Stir scallops and shrimp with any liquid in bowl into sauce in skillet and heat to boiling. Reduce heat and simmer until scallops and shrimp are just cooked through, about 2 minutes.

9. Transfer seafood to a clean bowl with slotted spoon and add linguine and cilantro to sauce in skillet, tossing to coat.

10. Divide pasta and sauce among 4 bowls. Top with seafood and sprinkle with scallion greens and chili mixture.

Seared Black Sesame-Crusted Tuna

SERVES 4

½ cup black sesame seed

¼ cup white sesame seed

4 (6 oz) ahi tuna steaks, 1 inch thick
salt and freshly ground black pepper

2 tablespoons extra virgin olive oil

2 eggs

DIPPING SAUCE

4 tablespoons coconut aminos (soy sauce substitute)

2 tablespoons water

1 tablespoon rice wine vinegar

1 tablespoon sesame oil

1 green onion, sliced

1. Whisk all the dipping sauce ingredients together and set aside.

2. In a shallow dish, combine the two types of sesame seeds and stir to mix.

3. In a separate bowl, beat 2 eggs.

4. Season the tuna with salt and pepper

5. Dip the fish in the egg mixture then in the sesame seeds, coating the tuna evenly.

6. In a nonstick pan, warm the oil until smoking, arrange the tuna in the pan (turn and cook until the white sesame seeds start to turn golden underneath (around 1 minute).

7. Carefully turn the tuna over and cook for about another minute.

8. Transfer the tuna to a cutting board and cut into ¼-inch-thick slices.

9. Serve immediately with dipping sauce.

One Pan Prawn Pilaf

SERVES 2

1 tablespoon extra virgin olive oil

2 tablespoons curry paste

1 small onion, finely chopped

1½ cups basmati rice, rinsed and drained

2½ cups chicken broth

1 (150g) pack frozen prawns defrosted

1 red chili, sliced into rings

handful of coriander leaves

lemon slices

1. Fry oil, curry paste and onions for 4–5 minutes.

2. Add rice to pan and stir to coat grains in curry and onions.

3. Add broth and bring to a boil.

4. Cover pan and turn down heat to low.

5. Allow to simmer for 12–15 minutes until liquid is absorbed and rice is cooked.

6. Turn off heat and stir in prawns and chili. Cover pan and leave to stand for 5 minutes.

7. Fluff up the rice grains with a fork.

8. Top with chopped coriander and lemon slices and serve.

Chicken Lettuce Wraps with Almond Chili Sauce (page 126)

CHICKEN

Chicken Lettuce Wraps

SERVES 2–4

2 teaspoons olive oil

½ pound boneless skinless chicken breasts (or tenders), chopped very small

4 cloves garlic, minced

½ cup yellow onion, chopped

½ teaspoon salt

¼ teaspoon freshly ground black pepper

1 carrot, shredded

½ cup cabbage, finely shredded

3 green onions, chopped

1 head iceberg, romaine or butter lettuce

ALMOND CHILI SAUCE

⅓ cup sweet chili sauce

1 tablespoon almond butter

½ teaspoon freshly grated ginger (or ¼ teaspoon ground ginger)

2 teaspoons coconut aminos (soy sauce substitute)

¼ cup fresh cilantro, chopped

crushed red pepper flakes to taste

1. Heat oil in a large skillet over medium.

2. Add chicken, garlic, onions, salt and pepper and cook, tossing occasionally, until chicken is cooked through.

3. Add the carrots, cabbage, and green onions, and cook for 2 more minutes.

4. In a small bowl combine the sweet chili sauce, ginger, almond butter, soy sauce, and crushed red pepper. Stir until smooth.

5. Add sauce to the pan. Add cilantro. Toss everything until combined.

6. Spoon mixture into individual lettuce cups. Should fill about 8 lettuce cups.

VARIATION
The cabbage and carrots in this recipe can be cooked or left fresh.

Chicken Cacciatore

SERVES 4–6

4 whole skinless boneless chicken breasts cut into pieces

⅓ cup rice flour

¼ cup extra virgin olive oil

1 garlic clove minced

1 red onion, sliced

1½ cups mushrooms, sliced

4 celery stalks, sliced

1 (28 oz) can tomatoes

½ cup white wine (optional)

1 teaspoon oregano

1 teaspoon basil

1 teaspoon parsley

1. Place chicken and rice flour in plastic bag and shake coating chicken.

2. In large non-stick fry pan add olive oil and cook chicken at medium heat till brown. Remove chicken.

3. To remaining oil in fry pan add minced garlic, onion, mushrooms, and sliced celery stalks. Sauté vegetables till soft.

4. Return chicken to fry pan and add can of tomatoes, wine (if using) and spices.

5. Simmer for 1 hour.

6. Serve on rice noodles or spinach.

Moroccan Chicken Casserole

SERVES 4

4–6 skinless, boned chicken breasts

1 tablespoon extra virgin olive oil

1 crushed clove of garlic

2 teaspoons paprika

2 teaspoons ground coriander

1 teaspoon ground ginger

¼ teaspoon ground cloves

2 onions, thinly sliced

2 medium sweet potatoes, peeled and diced

3 tablespoons arrowroot flour (or rice flour)

2 cups of chicken broth

salt and pepper to taste

chopped parsley to garnish

1. Preheat oven to 350°F.

2. Using paper towels pat the chicken pieces dry.

3. Heat oil over medium heat in large pan.

4. Add garlic and spices to the pan, stirring over a medium heat for 10–20 seconds.

5. Add chicken and cook 6–8 minutes, turning occasionally until coated with spices.

6. Transfer chicken to oven-proof dish, scattering vegetables over the chicken.

7. Mix arrowroot flour with chicken broth in fry pan, stir until thickened and boils. Remove pan from heat.

8. Season sauce with salt and pepper and pour over vegetables and chicken.

9. Cover with lid, and cook at 350°F for one hour, until chicken is cooked through.

Honey Mustard Chicken

SERVES 6

6 skinless boned chicken breasts

⅓ cup liquid honey

¼ cup canola oil (or extra virgin olive oil)

¼ cup Dijon mustard

2–4 teaspoons curry powder

1 pinch of cayenne pepper

1. Place chicken in a single layer in large oven-proof dish.

2. Combine honey, oil, mustard, curry powder and cayenne.

3. Pour over chicken.

4. Bake, uncovered, at 350°F for 20 minutes, basting once.

5. Turn chicken over, baste again and bake another 20 minutes or until internal temperature exceeds 165°F.

Chicken Cutlets with Olives & Tomatoes

SERVES 8

6 skinless boneless chicken breasts

6 cloves garlic, chopped

1 large onion, chopped

3 tablespoons extra virgin olive oil

juice of 1 lemon

1 (16 oz) can plum tomatoes, drained and chopped

18 black olives, drained, pitted and chopped (about ½ can)

3 tablespoons fresh parsley, chopped fine

2 teaspoons fresh thyme, chopped

salt and freshly ground pepper to taste

1. Set oven at 375°F and grease two 9 x 13 inch oven proof pans.

2. Marinate chicken in 2 tablespoons oil, lemon juice, salt and pepper for one hour, turning often.

3. In a large skillet sauté garlic and onions in remaining 1 tablespoon olive oil.

4. Add tomatoes and olives and sauté for 15 minutes, uncovered, stir often.

5. Add 1 tablespoon of the parsley and the thyme, stirring to mix.

6. Place the chicken breasts in the prepared pans and cover with sautéed mixture.

7. Sprinkle with remaining parsley.

8. Bake for 35–40 minutes in a 375°F oven or until brown and internal temperature exceeds 165°F.

Lemon Chicken

SERVES 4

4 whole skinless chicken breasts

½ cup extra virgin olive oil

salt and pepper to taste

½ teaspoon thyme

2 un-peeled lemons, thinly sliced

1. Halve chicken breasts and arrange in a 9 x 13 inch shallow, greased, baking dish.

2. Sprinkle with salt, pepper and thyme.

3. Pour olive oil over all.

4. Arrange lemon slices on top of chicken to cover all pieces.

5. Cook, uncovered for 1 hour at 350°F.

Grilled Chicken Kabobs

SERVES 4

6 boneless skinless chicken breasts (cut into 1 inch cubes)

MARINADE

1 cup vegetable oil

½ cup coconut aminos (soy sauce substitute)

¼ cup honey

¼ cup lemon juice

3 garlic cloves, sliced

½ teaspoon black pepper

1 pinch cayenne pepper or to taste (optional)

1. In a bowl mix together the oil with coconut aminos, honey, lemon juice, garlic slices, black pepper and cayenne.

2. Place the chicken cubes in the bowl and toss to coat with the marinade.

3. Cover and chill for 4 hours.

4. Remove the chicken from the marinade.

5. Pour marinade into a saucepan then remove the garlic slices and discard; boil for 10 minutes over medium-low heat (start timing the 10 minutes after boiling starts).

6. Thread the chicken onto metal skewers or wooden skewers that have been soaked in cold water for 30 minutes.

7. Place the skewers on a grill and cook for 18–20 minutes or until the chicken is cooked through, basting with cooked marinade during the last 10–12 minutes of cooking.

Orange Rosemary Chicken

SERVES 6

2 cloves of garlic

1 roasting chicken

1 orange, quartered

1 tablespoon fresh rosemary, chopped (or 1½ tablespoon dried rosemary)

1 tablespoon extra virgin olive oil

ROSEMARY BASTE

2 tablespoons orange marmalade

1½ tablespoon dried rosemary

1. Preheat oven to 325°F.

2. Peel garlic cloves and place in chicken cavity.

3. Stuff un-peeled orange wedges into cavity with fresh or dried rosemary.

4. Close the cavity and loosely tie legs together.

5. Place chicken on rack in roasting pan. Brush skin with oil.

6. Roast chicken, uncovered for two hours, basting frequently with pan juices.

7. Mix marmalade and rosemary to make the baste. Brush over chicken and continue roasting, basting with mixture, about 10 more minutes.

Baked Tarragon Chicken Breasts

SERVES 3–4

4 skinless, boneless chicken breasts

¼ cup extra virgin olive oil

¼ cup dry mustard

1 teaspoon tarragon

½ red onion, chopped

1 tablespoon parsley flakes

1. Preheat oven to 400°F.

2. Place chicken breasts in a 9 x 13 inch glass baking dish greased with olive oil.

3. Combine remaining ingredients and brush over chicken, covering completely. Cover with foil and bake for 50 minutes or until chicken is tender.

Gluten-Free Fried Chicken

SERVES 4–6

12 chicken drumsticks

2 eggs (or replacement)

1 cup rice flour

1 cup gluten-free breadcrumbs

2 teaspoons salt

2 cups canola oil (or olive oil)

1. Preheat oven to 375°F.

2. Mix eggs and salt in a bowl.

3. In a separate bowl, mix breadcrumbs and rice flour.

4. Pour oil into a deep roasting pan or dish and heat in oven for 15 minutes while preparing the chicken.

5. Dip each drumstick into egg mixture and then roll into breadcrumb mix. Carefully add to pan with heated oil.

6. Bake for 45 minutes at 375°F. Rotate drumsticks every 15 minutes.

7. Season to taste with salt and pepper.

8. Serve with a fresh salad and/or roasted potatoes.

TIP
Perfect for picnics! Also great served cold for lunch the next day.

Apple Mushroom Chicken

SERVES 6

¼ cup rice flour

2 teaspoons salt

¼ teaspoon pepper

dash of thyme

6 skinless, boneless chicken breasts

¼ cup canola oil (or mild tasting olive oil)

4 green onions, chopped

1 cup mushrooms, sliced

2 tablespoons lemon juice

1 teaspoon sugar

1 teaspoon salt

⅓ cup apple juice

1. Preheat oven to 325°F.

2. Mix flour, salt, pepper and thyme in a plastic bag.

3. Add chicken to bag and shake to coat well.

4. In fry pan, brown chicken in oil and transfer to casserole dish.

5. Add green onions and mushrooms to fry pan.

6. Cover and simmer for 3 minutes.

7. Add mixture to casserole dish.

8. Mix lemon juice, sugar, salt and apple juice.

9. Pour over chicken and bake at 325°F for one hour.

Oven-Baked Paprika Chicken

SERVES 4

4 chicken breasts (6 oz each)

2 tablespoons extra virgin olive oil

SEASONING

1½ tablespoons brown sugar

1 teaspoon paprika

1 teaspoon dried oregano (or thyme, or other herb of choice)

¼ teaspoon garlic powder

½ teaspoon each salt and pepper

parsley for garnish, finely chopped (optional)

1. Preheat oven to 425°F.

2. Pound chicken to ¾ inch at the thickest part—using a rolling pin, meat mallet or even your fist (key tip for even cooking and tender chicken).

3. Mix seasoning.

4. Line tray with foil and baking paper. Place chicken upside down on tray. drizzle chicken with about 1 tablespoon oil. Rub over with fingers. Sprinkle with seasoning.

5. Flip chicken, drizzle with 1 tablespoon of oil, rub with fingers, sprinkle with seasoning.

6. Refrigerate chicken for 30–60 minutes to allow spices to permeate chicken.

7. Bake 18 minutes, or until surface is golden or internal temperature is 175°F using a meat thermometer.

8. Remove from oven and immediately transfer chicken to serving plates.

9. Wait 3–5 minutes before serving. Garnish with freshly chopped parsley if desired.

Shepherds Pie (page 144)

BEEF, PORK, LAMB

Shepherd's Pie

SERVES 6

5 cups potatoes, cooked and mashed

3 tablespoons dairy-free margarine

1 tablespoon olive oil

1 onion, chopped

1 clove garlic, minced

1 teaspoon onion salt

1 teaspoon thyme

1 teaspoon rosemary

¼ teaspoon salt

¼ teaspoon pepper

1 pound lean ground beef (or ground lamb or ground turkey)

½ cup carrots, finely chopped

½ cup celery, finely chopped

½ cup mushrooms, finely chopped

½ cup zucchini, finely chopped

¼ cup red wine

1 cup beef broth

2 tablespoons of ketchup

2 tablespoons Worcestershire Sauce (French's is gluten-free)

1. Preheat oven to 375°F.

2. Peel potatoes and boil until fully cooked. Strain and mash well with margarine. Set aside.

3. Heat oil in fry pan over medium heat. Add onion, garlic, thyme, rosemary, salt and pepper. Stir and cook for 5 minutes.

4. Add meat to pan and cook until brown.

5. Stir in carrots, celery, mushrooms and zucchini and cook for 5 minutes.

6. Add in red wine, beef broth, ketchup and Worcestershire sauce. Keep stirring for 10–15 minutes to let the mixture reduce and thicken.

7. Transfer meat mixture to a 9 x 13 inch baking dish.

8. Spread mashed potatoes evenly over the meat mixture.

9. Drizzle 1 tablespoon of olive oil over top before baking at 375°F for 30 minutes or until potatoes start to brown.

10. For a crispier top, turn oven to broil for 1–2 minutes until potatoes are golden brown.

Homemade Spaghetti Sauce

SERVES 6–8

1½ pounds extra lean ground beef
(or ground turkey)

3 cloves garlic, minced

1 large onion, diced

1 cup mushrooms, diced

1 cup celery, chopped

1 cup carrots, chopped

1 cup spinach

1 can black olives

½ cup red wine

1 tablespoon onion powder

1 tablespoon Italian seasoning

2 (680 ml) cans (6 cups) tomato sauce

3 cups whole tomatoes, canned

1 (369 ml) can tomato paste

2 tablespoons olive oil

1. In a large pot heat olive oil then add garlic, onion, mushrooms, celery and carrots. Cook until soft.

2. Add ground beef (or turkey) and fry until browned.

3. Stir in spinach and olives and cook for 2 minutes.

4. Add red wine, onion powder and Italian seasoning. Reduce for 5–10 minutes.

5. Add tomato sauce, canned tomatoes and tomato paste and bring to a boil.

6. Reduce heat and simmer for 2 hours stirring regularly to prevent burning.

7. Serve over gluten-free or zucchini noodles.

Beef Stroganoff

SERVES 6

1½ pounds beef stir fry strips

1 tablespoon olive oil

2 large red onions, sliced

1 cup red wine

2 cups mushrooms, chopped

1 tablespoon Worcestershire sauce (gluten-free)

2 (900 ml) cartons beef broth

1 teaspoon dry mustard

2 tablespoons ketchup

2 tablespoons rice flour

½ cup dairy-free sour cream (optional)

1. In a large pot, over medium/high heat add olive oil and sliced onions, sauté until soft.

2. Add beef and stir gently until brown.

3. Pour in the red wine and boil for 5 minutes.

4. Add mushrooms, Worcestershire sauce, beef broth, dry mustard and ketchup. Bring to a boil then reduce to a high simmer for 1 hour.

5. Reduce heat to a low simmer and add dairy-free sour cream if desired.

6. In a small bowl add rice flour to ¼ cup of water, stir to make paste and slowly add to the stir fry mix to thicken.

7. Serve over spinach, gluten-free noodles or rice.

Cabbage Rolls

SERVES 6

1 large cabbage

1½ pounds ground beef (or ground turkey)

1 tablespoon olive oil

1 pack turkey bacon, cut into small pieces

1 (16oz) can tomato sauce

3 cups rice, cooked

1 large onion, diced

1 tablespoon sage

1 tablespoon thyme

1 garlic clove, minced

½ cup dairy-free swiss or mozza substitute (optional)

1. Preheat oven to 350°F

2. Cook 3 cups of rice following package instructions.

3. While rice is cooking, heat oil in fry pan and add diced onions and turkey bacon.

4. Add ground beef (or turkey) and brown.

5. Add sage, thyme and garlic.

6. Core cabbage and steam in a large pot of water until leaves are soft. Strain and blanch with cold water and set aside.

7. Add cooked rice to the beef mixture.

8. Stir and add more spices to taste.

9. Gently remove each cabbage leaf and spoon meat mixture into the centre.

10. Roll up tightly and place in a greased casserole dish.

11. Once, all the rolls are in the dish, pour tomato sauce over and cover with lid or tin foil.

12. Bake at 350°F for 60 minutes.

TIP

Can double the recipe and freeze one before baking for a quicker future meal. Defrost before baking or cook for 90 minutes from frozen.

Lettuce Wrap Tacos

SERVES 4

2 pounds ground beef (or ground turkey)

1 tablespoon cumin

1 tablespoon onion powder

1 tablespoon garlic powder

1 tablespoon chili powder

1 tablespoon olive oil

1 head butter lettuce (green leaf or iceberg lettuce would work as well)

FIXING OPTIONS

salsa

red onion, finely chopped

red cabbage, finely sliced

avocado, sliced

guacamole

cilantro

jalapeños

Spanish rice (rice cooked with ½ tomato sauce for liquid)

1. Fry meat with spices until fully cooked.

2. Carefully peel head of lettuce keeping each leaf whole.

3. Add meat mixture and your choice of fixings to lettuce leaf. Wrap and enjoy!

VARIATION

Can substitute with tilapia (or any other light white fish) for delicious fish tacos.

Grandma's Meatballs

SERVES 6

1 egg, beaten

1½ tablespoons coconut aminos

1 tablespoon honey

½ teaspoon salt

⅓ cup gluten free breadcrumbs

1 pound ground beef

1. Preheat oven to 325°F.

2. Combine first 5 ingredients.

3. Add meat and mix well.

4. Shape into 12 meatballs.

5. Place meatballs on greased baking sheet.

6. Bake in oven for 20 minutes, then turn meatballs and cook for 20 minutes.

7. Turn again and cook for another 20 minutes.

TIPS

• Kids love these served with rice and steamed or fresh vegetables.

• Add them to a spaghetti sauce and gluten free noodles.

• Make extra for lunch the next day or freeze for future meals.

Everyday Meat Loaf

SERVES 6

1½ pounds ground beef

2 beaten eggs

¾ cup rice dream

⅔ cup fine gluten-free dry breadcrumbs

2 tablespoons grated onion

1 teaspoon salt

½ teaspoon ground sage

dash of pepper

SAUCE

¼ cup ketchup

2 tablespoons brown sugar

1 teaspoon dry mustard

¼ teaspoon ground nutmeg

1. Preheat oven to 350°F.

2. Combine eggs, rice dream, breadcrumbs, onion, salt, sage and pepper.

3. Add beef and mix well.

4. Pat mixture into greased loaf dish.

5. Bake at 350°F for 1 hour.

6. Combine sauce ingredients.

7. Spread over meat loaf.

8. Bake 15 minutes longer.

Sweet Chili Lettuce Wraps

SERVES 6–8

1½ pounds extra lean ground beef (or ground turkey)

2 cups rice, cooked

2 red peppers, diced

1 large onion, diced

3 tablespoons sweet chili sauce

3 cloves garlic, minced

1 tablespoon olive oil

1 head of butter lettuce

3 tablespoons coconut aminos (soy sauce substitute)

1. In a large fry pan combine oil, garlic and onion.

2. Cook rice in a separate pot or rice cooker (see rice package for cooking instructions).

3. Add beef to pan and fry until brown.

4. Add red pepper and cook until tender.

5. Add sweet chili sauce and stir well. Reduce heat to simmer.

6. Carefully pull each full leaf of head of lettuce and wash under cold water. Pat dry with paper towel.

7. Stir in cooked rice to mixture.

8. Spoon mixture into each lettuce wrap and enjoy.

Pork Tenderloin with Mushroom-Marsala Sauce

SERVES 6

1¼ pound pork tenderloin, trimmed of fat and surface membrane

salt and freshly ground pepper

2 tablespoons olive oil

¼ cup rice flour

3 tablespoons margarine (or extra virgin olive oil)

½ pound mushrooms, sliced

2 shallots, finely chopped

¼ teaspoon dried sage

½ teaspoon dried rosemary

½ cup dry Marsala (or white wine)

1 cup beef broth

1. Cut pork crosswise in ½ inch (1.2 cm) slices. Pound lightly with a meat pounder or rolling pin until meat is about ⅓ inch (0.8 cm) thick. Sprinkle with salt and pepper.

2. Heat oil in large, heavy frying pan over medium-high heat. Dip pork in flour to coat. Cook meat in hot oil, turning once, until browned on both sides, for about 3 minutes.

3. Transfer meat to a plate.

4. Add 2 tablespoons of margarine (olive oil) to the pan drippings and cook mushrooms, stirring until they give off their liquid and it evaporates, about 6 minutes.

5. Add shallots, sage and rosemary and cook until shallots soften, for about 1 minute.

6. Add Marsala (or white wine) and broth; bring to a boil. Return pork to pan and cook, turning pork, until liquid thickens slightly, about 2 minutes.

7. Remove pan from heat, stir in remaining 1 tablespoon of margarine (or oil); add salt and pepper to taste.

8. Serve hot with mashed potatoes, rice or rice noodles and salad.

Honey Garlic Pork Chops

SERVES 6

½ cup ketchup

2–3 tablespoons honey

2 tablespoons coconut aminos

2 garlic cloves minced

6 (1-inch-thick) pork chops

1. Preheat grill to medium heat and lightly oil the grate.

2. Whisk ketchup, honey, coconut aminos, and garlic together in a bowl to make a glaze.

3. Sear the pork chops on both sides on the preheated grill.

4. Lightly brush glaze onto each side of the chops as they cook; grill until no longer pink in the center, about 7 to 9 minutes per side.

5. An instant-read thermometer inserted into the center should read 145°F.

Pork Chops with Italian Sausage

SERVES 6

4 thick cut pork chops

salt and pepper to taste

1 tablespoon extra virgin olive oil

¼ pound gluten-free sweet Italian sausage

1 small onion slivered

¼ pound mushrooms sliced

1 clove garlic minced

½ teaspoon Italian seasoning

¼ cup dry red wine

1 (8 oz) can tomato sauce

1. Preheat oven to 375°F.

2. Sprinkle pork chops with salt and pepper.

3. In a large frying pan, brown pork chops well in olive oil.

4. Remove chops from pan and set aside.

5. Pour off and discard all but 1 tablespoon pan drippings.

6. Remove casing from sausage and crumble meat into same pan.

7. Mix in onions and mushrooms. Cook, stirring until onions and sausage brown slightly.

8. Stir in garlic and Italian seasoning.

9. Pour in wine and tomato sauce and stir.

10. Place pork chops in casserole dish, spooning sausage mixture over them.

11. Cover with foil and bake for 45 minutes.

Marinated Lamb Kabobs

SERVES 6

1 boneless leg of lamb (about 5 pounds)

MARINADE

½ cup extra-virgin olive oil

¼ cup lemon juice

¼ cup honey

6 cloves garlic, finely chopped

1 large white onion, finely chopped

¼ cup chopped fresh mint leaves

2 tablespoons fresh oregano leaves, chopped

2 teaspoons fresh rosemary leaves, chopped

KABOBS

2 large white onions, cut into 2-inch squares

1 green bell pepper, cut into 2-inch squares

1 orange bell pepper, cut into 2-inch squares

1 red bell pepper, cut into 2-inch squares

1 yellow bell pepper, cut into 2-inch squares

1 pint cherry tomatoes, stemmed

1 (8 oz) package white button mushrooms

1. Soak wooden skewers in water for 30 minutes (or use metal skewers).

2. Trim all fat from the lamb and cut into 2-inch cubes.

3. Combine marinade ingredients in a large resealable plastic bag and mix well.

4. Add the lamb cubes to the bag, tossing to coat. Seal bag and marinate in the refrigerator at least 2 hours, preferably overnight, rotating the bag occasionally to continually coat the lamb.

5. Preheat an outdoor grill to medium heat. Remove lamb from refrigerator about 30 minutes before grilling to bring the meat to room temperature.

6. To assemble the kabobs: fill skewers, alternating peppers, lamb, tomatoes, onions and mushrooms until all ingredients are used.

7. Grill skewers, rotating to char lamb on all sides, until cooked to desired doneness, about 7 to 8 minutes for medium-rare.

Lamb Rib Chops with Curry Sauce

SERVES 6

2 racks of lamb, cut into individual chops or "popsicles"

CURRY SAUCE

1 cup mayonnaise (egg free if required)

2 teaspoons curry powder

1 teaspoon lime juice

1. In a sauce pan on low heat, stir mayonnaise, curry powder and lime juice together until fully mixed and slightly warm.

2. Grill lamb popsicles on medium heat for 5 minutes a side, set aside under tin foil to rest while making the sauce.

3. Serve lamb using the sauce as a dipping sauce or poured over lamb.

VARIATION

If you are avoiding eggs and therefore mayonnaise, the grilled lamb is delicious simply dipped in balsamic vinegar or mint sauce.

VEGETABLES

Maple Roasted Brussels Sprouts with Bacon

SERVES 6

2 pounds Brussels sprouts, trimmed

½ cup extra virgin olive oil

6 tablespoons maple syrup

6–8 slices bacon, cut into ½ inch pieces

1 teaspoon salt

½ teaspoon freshly ground pepper

1. Preheat oven to 400°F.

2. Place Brussels sprouts in a single layer in a baking dish. Drizzle with olive oil and maple syrup; toss to coat.

3. Partially fry bacon.

4. Sprinkle bacon over Brussels sprouts.

5. Season with salt and black pepper.

6. Roast in the preheated oven until bacon is crispy and Brussels sprouts are caramelized, 45 minutes, stirring halfway through.

7. Aluminum foil can be used to keep moist, cook it evenly, and makes clean-up easier.

No Big Dill Carrots

SERVES 4

2 cups baby carrots

1 tablespoon dried dill

1 tablespoon lemon juice

1. Steam carrots and serve topped with a sprinkle of dill and lemon juice.

Steamed Fresh Vegetables

SERVES 4

2 medium carrots, peeled and sliced

2 medium parsnips, peeled and sliced

1 stalk broccoli, cut in florets

8 mushrooms

1 tablespoon extra virgin olive oil

salt and freshly ground pepper

1. Steam carrots and parsnips for 3–5 minutes or until tender-crisp.

2. Add broccoli and mushrooms. Steam for 3 minutes or until broccoli is bright green.

3. Transfer to serving bowl, sprinkle with olive oil and salt and pepper to taste.

TIP
Other vegetables to substitute or add: celery, fennel, cauliflower, zucchini, cabbage or Brussels sprouts.

Roasted Vegetables

SERVES 8

2 large leeks, sliced in strips length wise

4 carrots, sliced length wise

3 tomatoes, halved

4 parsnips, sliced length wise

2 cups broccoli spears

extra virgin olive oil

2 cups whole mushrooms

1. Arrange vegetables in greased large baking sheet.

2. Cover vegetables with oil.

3. Bake at 375°F for 1 hour or till vegetables are tender and nicely brown. Stir occasionally.

TIP
Any of your favourite vegetables can be used.

Salad Rolls

SERVES 4

8 rice paper wraps

2 avocados

3 carrots, shredded

1 cucumber

¼ purple cabbage, thinly sliced

1 head butter leaf lettuce (or romaine)

basil leaf for garnish (optional)

sweet chili sauce for dipping (optional)

1. Cut up or shred all veggies.

2. Run dried rice paper wrap under warm water and lay flat on a wooden cutting board.

3. Place a row of sliced avocados then one leaf of lettuce.

4. Place the rest of the veggies on top of lettuce.

5. Once rice paper wrap is softened, carefully roll the wrap folding the ends in first.

6. Repeat for each roll.

7. Garnish with fresh basil leaf and serve with spicy chili sauce.

TIPS
• Add chicken or shrimp as a protein.

• Make extra for lunch the next day.

Mushroom Asparagus Risotto

SERVES 4–6

2 cups arborio rice

1 tablespoon olive oil

2 cloves garlic, minced

1 large red onion, diced

2 cups mushrooms, diced

12 asparagus spears, cut into bite sized pieces

3 cups dry white wine

4 cups chicken broth

⅓ cup gluten-free and dairy-free parmesan cheese substitute (optional)

1. In a large skillet, heat olive oil and add minced garlic.

2. Add onions, mushrooms and asparagus and sauté until brown.

3. Add arborio rice to the mixture.

4. Slowly add the wine and broth. Stirring constantly over low heat.

5. Continue to cook and stir for 30 minutes or until rice and vegetables are done.

6. Garnish with shredded gluten and dairy-free parmesan cheese if desired.

Vegetable Stir Fry

SERVES 4–6

1 teaspoon olive oil

2 cups broccoli crowns, chopped

½ red onion, diced

1 cup mushrooms, diced

1 cup celery, diced

1 cup carrots, diced

SAUCE

1 cup vegetable broth

1 cup orange juice (or pineapple juice)

2 tablespoons coconut aminos (soy sauce substitute)

½ teaspoon garlic, minced

½ teaspoon ginger, minced

1 tablespoon sweet chili sauce (optional)

1. Chop all vegetables into bite-sized pieces and set aside.

2. In a small bowl mix sauce ingredients and set aside.

3. Heat oil in deep fry pan or wok. Sauté onions and mushrooms until soft.

4. Add in other vegetables. Stirring often, cook until they are tender and crisp.

5. Pour sauce over vegetable mixture and bring to a boil. Turn down and let simmer for 5 more minutes.

6. Serve over rice or rice noodles.

TIPS
• Add cashews or other nuts.

• Make extra for lunch the next day.

• Add a protein like chicken or lean beef strips if desired.

Oven Baked Parsnips French Fries

SERVES 6

8 parsnips, sliced lengthwise and halved in shape of French fries

¼ cup extra virgin olive oil

1. Grease baking sheet with olive oil.

2. Place parsnip fries in microwave dish and microwave for 1 minute.

3. Spread parsnips on baking sheet.

4. Bake in hot oven at 425°F turning frequently for 5–10 minutes.

Savory Warm Mushrooms in Wine Sauce

SERVES 4

3 tablespoons extra virgin olive oil

1 pound small mushrooms

pepper to taste

1 clove garlic, minced

3 tablespoons white wine

1 teaspoon lemon juice

1 tablespoon parsley flakes

1. Wash mushrooms well and cut off stems.

2. In a skillet, heat olive oil on low heat.

3. Place mushroom caps in heated olive oil and add pepper and garlic.

4. Simmer for five minutes.

5. Add wine and lemon juice.

6. Cover and let stand for five minutes.

7. Sprinkle with parsley.

Steamed Fennel with Zucchini, Carrots & Green Onions

SERVES 6

6 green onions, cut in half lengthwise then cut into 2 inch lengths

2 cups each julienne (thin strip) carrots, fennel, and zucchini

1 tablespoon extra virgin olive oil

salt and pepper to taste

1. Steam all vegetables for 6 to 8 minutes.

2. Transfer to serving dish and toss with olive oil and salt and pepper to taste. The mild taste of fennel makes a pleasing addition to zucchini and carrots.

Zucchini Bake

SERVES 6

6–8 medium zucchinis, sliced thinly
4 juicy ripe tomatoes, chopped
2 cloves garlic crushed
3 tablespoons extra virgin olive oil
sea salt and freshly ground black pepper
½ cup gluten-free breadcrumbs

1. Heat oil in pan.

2. Add garlic and zucchini slices.

3. Sauté gently for 3–5 minutes.

4. Place in shallow oven-proof dish.

5. Add chopped tomatoes to pan with seasonings, simmer for 5 minutes.

6. Pour mixture over zucchini.

7. Top with breadcrumbs. Sprinkle top with a small amount of oil, and broil for 2 minutes to crisp breadcrumbs.

BBQ Veggie Kabobs

SERVES 6

2 large bell peppers (red, orange or yellow)

1–2 medium red or sweet white onions

½–1 pound mushrooms

1–2 zucchinis

½ pound cherry tomatoes

2 tablespoons olive oil

2 tablespoons lemon juice

Metal skewers

1. Chop all your vegetables so they are approximately equal in size and shape.

2. When threading vegetables on skewers, alternate between different vegetables, leaving a small space between each end with a mushroom to secure vegetables on skewer.

3. Place vegetables skewers on baking sheet.

4. Mix olive oil and lemon juice together.

5. Brush mixture over vegetable skewers with and refrigerate one hour before grilling.

6. Cook skewers on preheated grill until vegetables are tender, turning and basting vegetables with olive oil mixture occasionally. Grill for 10–15 minutes.

TIP

For kabobs you can cook meat and vegetables separately, so you have more control over different cooking times of the meat i.e. rare, medium rare, well done. Or you can mix the meat and vegetables on the same skewer if preferred.

*See Steak Kabobs recipe on page 215

Fried Rice

SERVES 6

3 cups rice, cooked (one day old rice works best)

1 large onion

2 cloves of garlic, minced

1 cup mushrooms, diced

½ cup carrots (fresh or frozen), diced small

3 tablespoons olive oil

2 tablespoons coconut aminos (optional)

1. In a large fry pan, add olive oil, garlic and diced onion.

2. Add mushrooms and carrots and sauté.

3. Add coconut aminos (optional).

4. Fold in cooked rice until entirely mixed and fry until rice starts to crisp.

VARIATION
Can add cubed rotisserie chicken for protein.

Beef Stew (page 180)

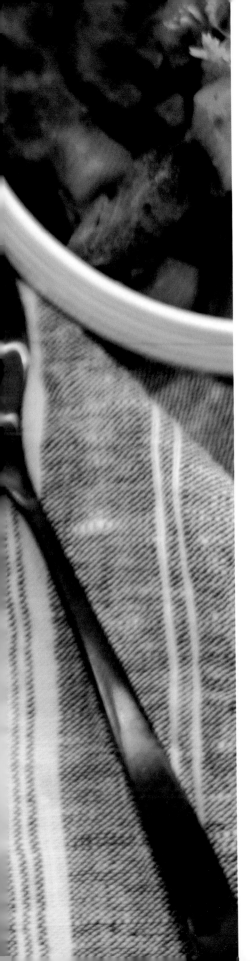

SLOW COOKING

Beef Stew

SERVES 7

2 pounds beef stew meat, cut into
1 inch cubes

2 tablespoons olive oil

1 teaspoon each salt and freshly ground
black pepper

1 large onion, finely chopped

3 medium celery stalks, sliced

2–3 cloves of garlic, minced

1 (6 oz) can tomato paste

3 cups low-sodium beef broth

1 beef bouillon cube

1 tablespoon Worcestershire sauce
(French's is gluten-free)

1 tablespoon coconut aminos (soy
sauce substitute)

1 teaspoon dried thyme

¾ teaspoon dried rosemary

1 bay leaf

4–6 potatoes, cut in bite-sized pieces

2 cups carrots, cut in bite-sized pieces

1 cup zucchini, chopped

¼ cup rice flour

¼ cup water

SLOW COOKER

1. Heat 1 tablespoon olive oil in an extra-large skillet over medium-high. Brown half of the meat in hot oil. Remove from skillet. Brown remaining meat in remaining oil.

2. Transfer beef to slow cooker.

3. In remaining oil, sauté onions and celery for 3 minutes. Add garlic and sauté 30 seconds longer then add in tomato paste and cook, stirring constantly for 1 minute.

4. Pour 1 cup beef broth into skillet along with Worcestershire sauce, bouillon cube, coconut aminos, thyme, rosemary and bay leaf.

5. Add potatoes and carrots over beef layer in slow cooker.

6. Then pour broth mixture in skillet into slow cooker along with remaining 2 cups beef broth.

7. Season lightly with salt and pepper.

8. Cover and cook on low heat for 8–10 hours or high for 6–7 hours.

9. About 30 minutes before serving, mix the flour and water together in a small bowl. Pour mixture into slow cooker until thickened slightly.

10. Add chopped zucchini.

11. Cover and cook on high heat for 20–30 minutes (remove bay leaf).

Lemon Chicken

SERVES 6

6 chicken breasts, cut into serving sizes

¼ cup rice flour

1¼ teaspoons salt

2 tablespoons extra virgin olive oil

1 (6 oz) can frozen lemonade concentrate, thawed

3 tablespoons brown sugar

3 tablespoons ketchup

1 tablespoon vinegar

2 tablespoons cold water

2 tablespoons rice flour

SLOW COOKER

1. Combine the flour with salt; coat chicken thoroughly.

2. Heat oil in a fry pan and brown chicken pieces on all sides.

3. Transfer chicken to slow cooker.

4. Stir together the lemonade concentrate, brown sugar, ketchup, and vinegar.

5. Pour over chicken in slow cooker.

6. Cover; cook on high-heat setting for 3–4 hours.

7. Remove chicken and then transfer the liquid to a saucepan.

8. Return chicken to cooker; cover to keep warm.

9. Skim fat from reserved liquid.

10. Blend cold water slowly into rice flour; stir into hot liquid.

11. Cook and stir till thickened and bubbly.

12. Serve chicken with sauce over rice and with a salad.

Porcupine Meatballs

SERVES 6

2 pounds hamburger

1 cup uncooked rice

⅔ cup onion, chopped

2 teaspoons salt

1 teaspoon celery salt

¼ teaspoon black pepper

2 eggs

2 liters or 2 packages of Imagine Creamy Tomato Soup (gluten-free)

2 (5.5 oz) cans tomato paste

1 cup water

4 teaspoons Worcestershire sauce (French's is gluten-free)

SLOW COOKER

1. Combine first 7 ingredients, mix well.

2. Shape hamburger mixture into 1½ inch balls.

3. Place meatballs in slow cooker.

4. Mix soup, tomato paste, water and Worcestershire sauce and pour over meatballs.

5. Cover and cook on low for 7–8 hours.

Butter Chicken

SERVES 4–6

1 pound boneless, skinless chicken breast or chicken thighs

1 medium onion, diced

2 teaspoons coconut oil

4 cloves garlic, finely minced

1 teaspoon fresh ginger, finely minced

1 teaspoon coriander

1 teaspoon cumin

1 teaspoon cardamom

½ teaspoon salt

¼–½ teaspoon cayenne pepper (optional)

1 (14 oz) can coconut milk

1 (6 oz) can tomato paste

juice of 1 lime

¼ cup cilantro (or to taste)

SLOW COOKER

1. In a medium sauté pan, heat coconut oil over medium heat.

2. Add onion and sauté until translucent and tender.

3. Add garlic, ginger, spices, and salt. Cook 1 minute longer, till all the spices are fragrant.

4. Stir in coconut milk and tomato paste and stir until well combined.

5. Add chicken to the slow cooker. Pour sauce over everything.

6. Cook on high heat for 3–4 hours or on low heat for 6–8 hours.

7. Shred or dice chicken into the sauce.

8. Squeeze in lime juice, top with cilantro.

9. Serve with your favourite vegetable and rice.

Lamb Curry

SERVES 6

1 pound lamb shoulder or lamb roast,
cut into ¾ inch cubes

¼ cup gluten-free flour mix

salt and pepper to taste

2 tablespoons olive oil

1 large onion, chopped

2 garlic cloves, crushed

1-inch piece fresh ginger, minced

1 long red chili, finely chopped

¼ cup Indian madras curry paste

1 can (400 ml) coconut milk

1 vegetable stock cube

1 cinnamon stick

1 dried bay leaf

3 carrots, chopped in bite size pieces

3 potatoes, chopped in 1½ inch pieces

Steamed white rice, to serve

Dairy-free yogurt to serve (optional)

SLOW COOKER

1. Place flour and lamb in a plastic bag.

2. Add salt and pepper. Shake to coat.

3. Heat oil in a saucepan over medium-high heat.

4. Cook lamb, in batches, for 3 to 4 minutes or until browned.

5. Transfer to a 4.5 liter-capacity slow cooker.

6. Add onion, garlic and ginger to pan. Cook, stirring, for 4 to 5 minutes or until tender.

7. Add chili and curry paste. Cook, stirring for 1 minute or until fragrant.

8. Add coconut milk, vegetable stock cube and ¾ cup cold water.

9. Bring to a boil.

10. Transfer to slow cooker. Add cinnamon stick and bay leaf. Stir to combine.

11. Add carrots and potatoes 2 hours before the end of cooking time.

12. Cook, covered, on low for 6 hours or until lamb is tender.

13. Remove and discard cinnamon stick and bay leaf. Serve with dairy-free yogurt if desired.

Pork Tenderloin

SERVES 4–6

2 pounds of pork tenderloin

¼ cup coconut aminos (soy sauce substitute)

1½ tablespoons yellow mustard

2 tablespoons olive oil

3 tablespoons maple syrup

1 shallot, chopped

1 teaspoon onion powder

1 garlic clove, minced

SLOW COOKER

1. Turn slow cooker on to low.

2. In large bowl, mix the coconut aminos, mustard, oil, maple syrup, shallot, onion powder and garlic together to make the marinade.

3. Place tenderloin in slow cooker and pour the marinade over.

4. Cook on low for about 5 hours for two small tenderloins or 6 hours for one large piece.

5. Turn the pork twice to ensure even cooking at 2 hours and 4 hours.

6. Slice and serve pouring the juices over the meat.

Orange Marmalade Chicken

SERVES 6

3–4 boneless chicken breasts, chopped in small pieces

3 tablespoons gluten-free flour mix

2 tablespoons extra virgin olive oil

1 teaspoon rice wine vinegar

2 tablespoons coconut aminos (soy sauce substitute)

½ teaspoon sesame oil

¾ cup orange marmalade

2 tablespoons brown sugar

½ teaspoon salt

sesame seeds for garnish (optional)

SLOW COOKER

1. In a bowl, mix the rice wine vinegar, coconut aminos, sesame oil, marmalade, brown sugar and salt. Set aside.

2. In a plastic bag, add the flour mix and the chicken. Shake to coat.

3. Pour oil in a skillet and brown the sides of the chicken.

4. Put the browned chicken in slow cooker.

5. Then cover the chicken with the sauce mixture and give the pot a stir.

6. Cook on low 4–5 hours or high 2–3 hours.

7. Serve topped with sesame seeds (optional).

Sweet and Sour Ribs

SERVES 8–10

¾ cup brown sugar

¼ cup rice flour

⅓ cup water

½ cup vinegar

2 tablespoons coconut aminos (soy sauce substitute)

¼ cup ketchup

½ teaspoon ground ginger

¼ teaspoon garlic powder

1 teaspoon salt

⅛ teaspoon pepper

3 pounds meaty pork spareribs, cut in 2–3 rib sections

SLOW COOKER

1. Mix brown sugar and rice flour in a saucepan.

2. Add water, then vinegar, coconut aminos, ketchup, ginger, and garlic powder.

3. Cook and stir over medium heat until boiling and thickened.

4. Layer ribs in 4–6-quart slow cooker, spooning sauce over each layer.

5. Cover and cook on low for 10–12 hours or on high for 5–6 hours until ribs are very tender.

Slow Cooked Veal with Salsa

SERVES 4

2 pounds veal, sliced ½ inch thick

6 large tomatoes, finely diced

1 yellow onion, minced

2 cloves garlic, minced

1 teaspoon black pepper

½ cup lime juice

1 teaspoon cayenne pepper

⅓ cup fresh cilantro, finely chopped

SLOW COOKER

1. To make the salsa, combine tomatoes, onion, garlic, pepper, lime juice, cayenne pepper and cilantro together and mix well. Makes 2 cups.

2. Place veal slices in slow cooker and cover with half the salsa.

3. Cook on low heat for 5 hours.

4. Remove from slow cooker and pour remaining salsa over meat before serving.

Cabbage Roll Soup (page 194)

INSTANT POT

Cabbage Roll Soup

SERVES 6

12 bacon slices, chopped into 1 inch pieces

1 pound ground beef (or chicken or turkey

1 onion, diced

1 tablespoon garlic, minced

1 (15 oz) can tomatoes, crushed or diced

1 (8 oz) can tomato sauce

1 tablespoon tomato paste

2 cups carrots (1 large carrot), grated

3 cups cabbage, chopped

1 teaspoon dried thyme

1 teaspoon dried oregano

1 teaspoon Italian seasoning

¼ teaspoon salt and pepper or to taste

4 cups low sodium beef broth (or chicken broth)

1 cup cooked rice

fresh parsley, chopped

INSTANT POT

1. Select Sauté and once Instant Pot reads Hot, add the chopped bacon. DO NOT stir for 1 minute.

2. Using a wooden spoon, start stirring frequently until the bacon is crisp.

3. Remove the bacon from the pot and drain grease. Wipe the edges and return pot to the Instant Pot and push bacon to one side of the pot.

4. Add the ground beef to the other side of the pot using a wooden spoon, break the beef and cook by stirring frequently for a few minutes, until no longer pink.

5. Carefully remove the pot from the Instant Pot and discard excess grease. Wipe the edges and return pot to the Instant Pot.

6. Add the onion and garlic and cook for 1–2 minutes, stirring occasionally.

7. Add the rest of the ingredients and stir to combine. Make sure you do not go over the max line of the pot once you add the broth.

8. Close the Instant Pot with the lid and lock it. Turn the steam vent to "sealing" and set it to cook for 10 minutes on High Pressure.

9. When the cook time is up, allow the pressure to reduce on its own without opening the steam release vent for 10 minutes. This is called Natural Pressure Release. After 10 minutes carefully release the rest of the pressure by opening the vent.

10. Open the lid and stir the soup. Taste and adjust for salt and pepper.

11. Once you add the soup to individual bowls, if desired, top with cooked rice and sprinkle chopped fresh parsley.

Spicy Carrot Soup

SERVES 2

8–10 large carrots, peeled and chopped coarsely

1 onion, chopped

3 cloves garlic, minced

1 (14 oz/400ml) can coconut milk

1½ cups chicken or veggie broth

¼ cup almond butter

1 tablespoon red curry paste

salt to taste

cilantro and toasted almonds for topping

INSTANT POT

1. Place all the ingredients in the Instant Pot.

2. Cook on Manual for 15 minutes.

3. When cooked do a controlled quick release.

4. Put mixture in blender and blend until smooth.

5. Season with salt to taste.

6. Top with cilantro and toasted almonds.

Vegetable Soup

SERVES 6

1 tablespoon olive oil

3 garlic cloves, minced

1 medium yellow onion, chopped

5 white mushrooms, washed and sliced

2 cups cauliflower florets

2 carrots, peeled and chopped

2 celery stalks, chopped

2 cups zucchini, chopped

3 cups cabbage, chopped

1 (15 oz) can diced tomatoes

3½ cups low sodium vegetable
or chicken broth

1 bay leaf

1 teaspoon Italian seasoning

½ teaspoon ground paprika

½ teaspoon black pepper

½ teaspoon salt

1 tablespoon lemon juice

¼ teaspoon cayenne pepper

½ teaspoon turmeric

INSTANT POT

1. Chop onion, carrots and celery, Mince garlic. Slice mushrooms. Set aside.

2. Press sauté button on your Instant Pot. Add olive oil to the pot. Wait 2 minutes for it to preheat.

3. Add garlic and onion to pot. Sauté, stirring often, until the onion softens. Add mushrooms and sauté for 2 minutes, until they are fragrant.

4. Press "off/stop" button.

5. Add remaining ingredients to Instant Pot.

6. Place lid on the Instant Pot and make sure the valve is set to "sealing".

7. Press "soup" setting and timer to 12 minutes.

8. The Instant Pot will beep and start cooking. It may take about 12 minutes for it to come to pressure and then start the timer.

9. When done, the Instant Pot will beep. Let the pressure release naturally for about 5 minutes, then quick release any remaining pressure by carefully switching the valve to "venting".

10. Carefully remove the lid, away from your face, and set aside.

11. Stir the soup. Let cool slightly before serving.

12. Season with more salt and pepper to taste.

Carrot Ginger Soup

SERVES 2

1 tablespoon olive oil

1 onion, chopped

2 garlic cloves, minced

2 tablespoons ginger, finely chopped

5 cups carrots, peeled and chopped

1 cup celery

2 cups vegetable broth

¾ teaspoon salt

½ teaspoon pepper

1 teaspoon dried thyme leaves

1 can (400ml/13.5 oz) coconut milk

juice of ½ lime

INSTANT POT

1. Cook onion in olive oil using sauté function on your Instant Pot for 5–6 minutes.

2. Add the garlic and ginger, cook 1–2 more minutes. Turn off sauté function.

3. Add carrots, celery, broth, salt, pepper and thyme and stir to combine.

4. Put the lid on, turn vent to sealed and cook on manual high pressure for 5 minutes.

5. Do a quick pressure release after time is up.

6. Blend until smooth in blender.

7. Add the coconut milk and lime juice.

8. Warm soup as needed.

New England Clam Chowder

SERVES 4–6

3 (6½ oz) cans chopped clams* (reserve clam juice) (or 1 pound of frozen clams can be used)

1 bottle clam juice

6 slices bacon, chopped

3 tablespoons extra virgin olive oil

½ cup carrots, diced

½ cup celery, chopped

½ cup onion, finely diced

¼ teaspoon dried thyme

2 cloves garlic, pressed or finely minced

¾ teaspoon salt

¼ teaspoon pepper

4 cups potatoes, diced

1⅓ cup Original Rice Dream

1½ tablespoons gluten-free flour mix for thickening

chopped chives for garnish

INSTANT POT

1. Open the cans of clams and drain the clam juice into a 2–cup measuring cup. Add clam juice to make 2 cups of liquid. Set the clams and juice aside.

2. Turn on the pressure cooker's Sauté function and add the chopped bacon. Cook, stirring occasionally, until fat has rendered out of it, but not crispy.

3. Add the olive oil, carrots, onion, celery, and thyme. Cook, stirring and scraping the bottom of the pot to get up all the brown bits, until the onion starts turning translucent.

4. Add the garlic, salt, and pepper. Cook for 1 minute, stirring frequently.

5. Add the potatoes, and clam juice and stir.

6. Put the lid on the pot and lock in place. Turn the steam release knob to the Sealing position.

7. Cancel the Sauté function.

8. Set to Pressure Cook/Manual and use the + or - (or dial) to choose 4 minutes (High Pressure). When cook time has ended, let the pot rest undisturbed for 2 to 3 minutes, then do a controlled Quick Release.

9. Turn the Sauté function back on.

10. Add the clams and the Rice Dream. Let the chowder heat through but try not to boil it.

11. If you want it thicker, you can thicken it with gluten-free mix mixed with some of clam juice. Mix well and stir it in.

12. Turn off the pot and garnish the clam chowder with chopped chives.

Beef Short Ribs

SERVES 3–4

1 teaspoon rosemary

1 teaspoon onion salt

½ teaspoon paprika

½ teaspoon ground pepper

½ teaspoon sage

2 pounds beef short rib

2 tablespoons extra virgin olive oil

1 (6 oz) can tomato paste

½ cup water

½ cup balsamic vinegar

2 tablespoons Dijon mustard

1 tablespoon unsweetened cocoa powder

3 cloves garlic, minced

INSTANT POT

1. Mix rosemary, onion salt, paprika, pepper and sage together. Rub on the outside of the beef short rib; set aside.

2. Set your Instant Pot to Sauté.

3. Drizzle oil into Instant Pot.

4. Using tongs, lower short ribs into Instant Pot.

5. Sear all sides.

6. Remove short ribs; set aside.

7. Add tomato paste, water, balsamic, Dijon mustard, cocoa, and garlic to the Instant Pot and mix with a spoon until combined.

8. Add short ribs.

9. Place lid on Instant Pot and lock into place.

10. Make sure your steam vent is turned to closed.

11. Set cooker to manual and set the timer for 40 minutes.

12. Once the 40 minutes are up, let the Instant Pot sit for 10 minutes.

13. Carefully turn the pressure release valve.

14. Once all the pressure is released, unlock the lid.

15. Spoon sauce over each piece of beef short rib and serve warm.

Salmon with Garlic Potatoes & Greens

SERVES 4

1¼ pounds small red-skinned potatoes, halved or quartered

4 tablespoons unsalted butter (dairy-free)

salt and freshly ground pepper

4 (5–6 oz) salmon fillets (¾–1 inch thick)

¼ teaspoon paprika

½ teaspoon grated lemon zest, plus wedges for serving

4 cloves garlic, minced

4 cups packed mixed baby spinach

1 cup water

INSTANT POT

1. Put the potatoes in the bottom of the Instant Pot. Add 1 cup water, 2 tablespoons butter, ½ teaspoon salt and a few grinds of pepper. Place the pot's steam rack over the potatoes.

2. Rub the top and sides of the salmon fillets with the paprika and lemon zest and season generously with salt and pepper. Place salmon on the rack. Put on the lid, making sure the steam valve is in the sealing position, and set the cooker to high pressure for 3 minutes. When finished, carefully turn the steam valve to the venting position to release the pressure.

3. Remove the salmon and rack and set the cooker to sauté at normal heat. When the potatoes start sizzling, add the garlic and cook, stirring, until softened, 1 to 2 minutes; stir in the remaining 2 tablespoons butter and season generously with salt and pepper. Smash the potatoes with a fork or wooden spoon until chunky.

4. Turn off the cooker. Add the mixed greens to the potatoes and stir until wilted, 1 to 2 minutes. Season with salt and pepper. Divide the salmon and potato mixture among plates. Serve with lemon wedges.

Spinach Soup

SERVES 8

1 (5 oz) bag of baby spinach

1 head fresh broccoli, chopped into florets

1 bunch kale, roughly chopped

1 tablespoon coconut oil

3 cloves garlic, minced

1 medium onion, diced

½ teaspoon ground cumin

6 cups vegetable broth

½ teaspoon paprika

2 cups light coconut milk

salt & pepper to taste

INSTANT POT

1. Thoroughly wash the broccoli, kale, and spinach. Set aside.

2. Turn your Instant Pot on the "Sauté" mode. Add the oil, onions, garlic, cumin, paprika, salt, and pepper. Sauté for 4 to 5 minutes, until the onions caramelize.

3. Turn off the "Sauté" function. Add the broccoli, kale and the vegetable broth. Put the lid back on to your Instant Pot and make sure that the pressure valve is in the "Sealing" position.

4. Select the manual mode and set for 5 minutes.

5. When Instant Pot beeps, use the "Quick release" way to let release the pressure. Use a thick kitchen towel while releasing the pressure to avoid burning yourself from the steam.

6. Next, add the bag of baby spinach to the broccoli and mix it in.

7. The heat from the steam will be enough to wilt the spinach.

8. Blend the soup either by using an immersion blender or regular blender. If you don't have an immersion blender, be careful when transferring your spinach soup ingredients to your regular blender. The contents will be very hot.

9. Return the soup to the Instant Pot. Turn on the "Sauté" mode again.

10. Add the coconut milk and simmer for 5 minutes. Also, check for seasoning and adjust the salt and pepper accordingly.

11. Serve hot.

Beef & Broccoli

SERVES 4

1½ pounds boneless chuck roast beef, sliced into thin strips

6–7 cups broccoli florets

1 garlic clove, minced

1 tablespoon fresh ginger, minced

1 tablespoon extra virgin olive oil

SAUCE

1 cup beef broth

⅓ cup coconut aminos (soy sauce substitute)

⅓ cup brown sugar

2 tablespoons gluten-free flour mix

INSTANT POT

1. Select the sauté mode add the extra virgin olive oil.

2. When the pot is hot, add the garlic, ginger and sliced beef.

3. Cook for a few minutes until browned, stirring frequently.

4. Add beef broth, coconut aminos and brown sugar.

5. Stir together to dissolve the sweetener, Turn off the sauté mode.

6. Secure and seal the lid. On manual cook for 15 minutes at high pressure.

7. While waiting, cook broccoli by microwaving for 3-4 minutes or steam until tender.

8. When cooking done, manually release pressure by carefully turning the release valve to its venting position.

9. Uncover the Instant Pot and remove ¼ cup of liquid. Mix it with gluten-free flour mix in a small bowl until completely dissolved and smooth and add it back to the pot.

10. Turn on the sauté mode. Let the sauce simmer for about 5 minutes to thicken it a bit, stirring frequently. Turn of the sauté mode.

11. Add cooked broccoli back to the pot and briefly stir to coat with the sauce.

12. Serve immediately with a side of rice or cauliflower rice.

Spinach Chicken

SERVES 3

2 cups marinara sauce (may use similar spaghetti sauce)

2 tablespoon olive oil

1 cup frozen spinach (or 4 cups fresh)

¾ pound chicken breasts (2 medium breasts, can use frozen)

INSTANT POT

1. Place the chicken breasts in the bottom of the Pot.

2. Layer the spinach over the chicken.

3. Pour marinara sauce over the top.

4. Close the Instant Pot lid and close steam valve.

5. Cook on Manuel for 10 minutes.

6. Allow for Natural Release of steam for about 10 minutes.

7. Remove lid and season with salt and pepper to taste.

8. Serve with a side of brown rice and a salad for a complete meal.

Porcupine Meatballs

SERVES 4

1 pound lean ground beef

½ cup uncooked rice

⅓ cup chopped onion

1 teaspoon salt

½ teaspoon celery salt

⅛ teaspoon black pepper

1 egg

1 package (1 litre) of Imagine Tomato Soup (dairy-free and gluten-free)

1 can tomato paste

¼ cup water

2 teaspoons Worcestershire sauce (French's is gluten-free)

INSTANT POT

1. Combine first 7 ingredients, mix well.

2. Shape hamburger mixture into 1½ inch balls.

3. Mix soup, tomato paste, water and Worcestershire sauce. Pour into the pot and turn on the Sauté mode to start the sauce to simmer.

4. When the sauce is just starting to simmer, stir it and carefully add the meatballs into the pot.

5. Cancel the Sauté mode. Close the lid on the Instant Pot and set the steam release knob to the sealing position.

6. Cook for 25 minutes on manual.

7. When the cooking time ends, let pot naturally release for 15 minutes.

8. Then manually release the remaining steam.

9. Serve meatballs with some sauce over them.

10. Meatballs go well with salad, or a vegetable.

SPECIAL OCCASIONS

Turkey Dinner

SERVES 10–15

**GLUTEN-FREE SAUSAGE
BREAD STUFFING**

1½ cups celery (3 stalks), chopped

12 oz gluten-free turkey or
chicken sausages

1 cup onion (1 large), chopped

½ cup margarine (dairy-free)

2 teaspoons poultry seasoning

¼ teaspoon black pepper

12 cups dry gluten-free dry bread cubes

3 apples, peeled and diced

1½ cup chicken broth

1. To make dry bread for stuffing, cut fresh
   bread or thawed out gluten-free bread
   into ½ cubes (12–14 slices of bread to
   make 8 cups of dry cubes) spread cubes
   on a baking sheet. Bake in a 300°F oven
   for 10–15 minutes or until bread cubes
   are dry, stirring twice; cool. (Bread will
   continue to dry and crisp as it cools).

2. In a large skillet cook sausage until
   brown. Drain; set aside.

3. In a large pot cook celery and
   onion in melted butter until tender
   but not brown.

4. Remove from heat.

5. Stir in poultry seasoning and pepper.

6. Add sausage.

7. Stir in dry bread cubes and apples.

8. Drizzle with enough chicken broth to
   moisten, toss lightly to combine. (use
   to stuff 15–20 pound turkey) or you can
   bake in casserole covered in a 325°F
   oven for 30–45 minutes or until
   heated through.

CRANBERRY SAUCE

2 cups fresh or frozen cranberries

1 cup fresh orange juice

¼ cup (or less) maple syrup or honey

1 cup blueberries

½ cup raspberries

½ cups strawberries

¼ cup sugar

1. In a large saucepan, stir together
   cranberries, orange juice, maple syrup
   and sugar. Bring to a gentle boil over
   medium-high heat.

2. Reduce the heat to low and simmer for
   15–20 minutes.

3. Add the blueberries and raspberries and
   cook for another 3 to 4 minutes.

4. Set aside to cool, then transfer to a
   jar and keep in the fridge until cold
   and thick.

MAKING THE TURKEY

18–20 pound turkey

1. Rinse the inside of turkey, pat dry with paper towel.

2. If desired, season body cavity with salt and pepper.

3. Spoon stuffing, if using, loosely in the neck and body cavity.

4. Place turkey, breast side up, on a rack in a shallow roasting pan.

5. Brush with oil.

6. Cover turkey loosely with foil.

7. Place turkey in a 325°F oven (4¼ to 4½ hours). Roast until internal temp 170°F.

8. Stuffed birds generally require 15–45 minutes roasting time than unstuffed birds.

9. During the last 45 minutes of roasting, remove the foil.

10. Remove turkey from oven. Cover, let stand for 15–20 minutes before carving.

GLUTEN-FREE GRAVY

2–4 cups chicken broth (low salt)

1 chicken bouillon cube

1–2 tablespoon gluten-free flour mix

salt and pepper

1. To make the gravy, remove the turkey from the pan.

2. Place pan on stove on medium high heat.

3. Leaving the drippings in pan, stir in 1 to 2 tablespoons of rice flour or gluten-free flour mix (add more flour if needed).

4. Stir with a wire whisk until the flour has thickened and the gravy is smooth.

5. Heat a cup of chicken broth and dissolve chicken bouillon cube in it.

6. Add the cup of chicken broth with the dissolved bouillon cube.

7. Continue to add chicken broth until gravy is the desired consistency.

8. Continue to cook slowly and stir constantly.

9. Season the gravy with salt and pepper.

Hot and Spicy Chicken Wings

SERVES 4

3 pounds chicken wings

½ cup ketchup

¼ cup water

¼ cup honey

¼ cup lemon juice

2 tablespoons Dijon mustard

1 tablespoon Worcestershire sauce
(French's is gluten-free)

2 tablespoons hot pepper sauce

2 cloves of garlic, minced

2 tablespoons dry minced onions

1. Cover a broiler pan with foil, poking holes in the foil.

2. Arrange wings in single layer. Place under broiler until lightly brown.

3. In a saucepan, mix all ingredients and bring to a boil. Reduce heat and simmer for 5 to 10 minutes.

4. Using tongs, dip each chicken wing in hot sauce and place on greased baking sheet.

5. Bake at 375°F for 35–40 minutes or until done.

6. Baste with remaining sauce during cooking.

7. During last few minutes, turn on broiler and crisp wings.

Easy Guacamole

SERVES 2

2 avocados

1 small onion, finely chopped

1 garlic clove, minced

1 ripe tomato, chopped

1 tablespoon fresh cilantro, chopped

juice of lime

salt and pepper to taste

jalapeño, remove seeds and finely chop (optional to taste)

1. Peel and mash avocados in a medium serving bowl.

2. Stir in onion, garlic, tomato, cilantro, salt and pepper.

3. Stir in lime juice.

4. Add chopped jalapeño if you prefer it spicy.

5. Chill for half an hour to blend flavours.

BBQ Steak Kabobs

SERVES 6

1½ pounds top sirloin steak or beef tenderloin, cut into 1½ inch cubes

Metal Skewers

TERIYAKI MARINADE

2 tablespoons olive oil

¼ cup coconut aminos (soy sauce substitute)

2 tablespoons firmly packed brown sugar

3 tablespoons dry sherry or red wine

1 teaspoon fresh ginger or ¼ teaspoon ground ginger

1 teaspoon salt

1 clove garlic, minced or pressed

WINE GARLIC MARINADE

1 cup dry red wine

2 tablespoons wine vinegar

2 cloves of garlic, minced or pressed

1 teaspoon oregano leaves

2 tablespoons olive oil

HERB-WINE MARINADE BASTE

⅓ cup tomato-based chili sauce (or ketchup)

¾ cup dry red wine

½ cup olive oil

1 tablespoon instant minced onion

1 tablespoon Worcestershire sauce

1 teaspoon crumbled dry rosemary

1½ teaspoon pepper

1. Choose a marinade and mix all ingredients in a bowl and add the meat. Marinade can be doubled depending on the amount of meat you are cooking.

2. Cover and chill in the fridge for at least 30 minutes, preferably several hours or even overnight.

3. Thread the meat onto the skewers.

4. Baste the kabobs with some of the remaining marinade.

5. Grill on high, direct heat. Grill for 8–10 minutes, depending on how done you would like your meat.

6. Let the meat rest for 5 minutes before serving.

TIP

For kabobs you can cook meat and vegetables separately, so you have more control over different cooking times of the meat i.e. rare, medium rare, well done. Or you can mix the meat and vegetables on the same skewer if preferred.

*See Veggie Kabobs recipe on page 176

Veal Scaloppini

SERVES 6

1½ pounds veal steak (½ inch thick)

¼ cup rice flour

¼ cup oil

1 medium onion, sliced thin

1 red pepper, cut in strips

1 (10 oz) chicken broth

½ pound mushrooms, sliced

1 tablespoon oil

parsley and lemon wedges (optional)

SAUCE

1 teaspoon salt

1 teaspoon paprika

½ cup extra virgin olive oil

¼ cup lemon juice

1 garlic clove, minced

1 teaspoon prepared mustard

¼ teaspoon nutmeg

½ teaspoon sugar

1. To make the sauce, combine salt, paprika, oil, lemon juice, garlic, mustard, nutmeg and sugar in a jar. Shake to combine thoroughly.

2. Cut veal into serving pieces.

3. Spread veal in shallow dish and pour sauce over. Coat well and let stand 20 minutes.

4. Heat oil in large skillet.

5. Lift veal from sauce and dip in flour.

6. Brown in skillet and add onion and red peppers.

7. Combine chicken broth with remaining sauce and pour over veal.

8. Continue cooking slowly (covered) until veal is tender (about 30 minute).

9. Brown mushrooms lightly in oil.

10. Add mushrooms to veal.

11. Serve on large platter surrounded with gluten-free noodles and garnish with parsley and lemon wedges.

Stuffed Chicken with Mushroom Sauce

SERVES 4–6

4–6 chicken breasts

8–10 slices of gluten-free bread, toasted

1 large onion, diced

2 garlic cloves, minced or pressed

3 tablespoons olive oil

1 tablespoon sage

1 tablespoon thyme

MUSHROOM SAUCE

2 tablespoons olive oil

2 large onions, diced

1 garlic clove, minced or pressed

2 pounds mushrooms, sliced

¾ cup white wine

1 cup chicken broth

2 tablespoons rice flour

2 tablespoons of water

1. Toast bread and set aside to cool.

2. In a fry pan, add 1 tablespoon of olive oil and sauté 1 diced onion and 2 cloves of garlic.

3. Cube bread to make breadcrumbs and add to oil and onions.

4. Add sage and thyme and stir stuffing until covered.

5. Pound each chicken breast flat and spoon 2 tablespoons of stuffing in the centre. Wrap chicken around the stuffing and secure with a small metal skewer.

6. In a pan, heat remaining 2 tablespoons of oil and brown the chicken on all sides before placing in a casserole dish.

7. Bake at 375°F for 45 min. Internal temperature of chicken should be 165°F

8. To make the mushroom sauce, heat 2 tablespoons of olive oil and 1 clove of garlic in a large sauce pan. Add 1 diced onion and sauté for 2 minutes.

9. Add sliced mushrooms and sauté for 10 minutes.

10. Add white wine and chicken broth. Turn heat down to simmer and reduce until liquid is halved.

11. Mix rice flour and water together. Stir paste into sauce and simmer on low until thickened.

12. Pour sauce over stuffed chicken and serve.

Lamb-Stuffed Grape Leaves

SERVES 8–10

¼ cup regular white rice uncooked

¼ cup onion, finely chopped

2 tablespoons snipped fresh mint leaves
(or 1 tablespoon dried mint, crushed)

2 tablespoons snipped parsley

1 teaspoon salt

½ pound ground lamb

24 fresh or canned grape leaves

2 tablespoons canola oil

2 cups water

cheesecloth (for lining the slow cooker)

SLOW COOKER

1. Combine rice, onion, mint, parsley, ¼ teaspoon salt, 3 tablespoon water, dash of pepper.

2. Add lamb; mix well.

3. Rinse fresh grape leaves; drain and open flat.

4. Spoon 1 tablespoon filling in center of each leaf.

5. Fold in sides; roll up.

6. Line slow cooker with double thickness of cheesecloth.

7. Place stuffed leaves in cooker.

8. Mix oil, remaining ¾ teaspoon salt and 2 cups water; pour over to cover grape leaves.

9. Tie corners of cheesecloth together.

10. Cover; cook on high-heat setting for 2½ hours.

11. Remove and place stuffed leaves on platter, garnish with lemon slices or cherry tomatoes.

TIP
This recipe can be doubled and is a real favourite at pot-lucks.

Stuffed Mushroom Caps

SERVES 8–10

20 large whole fresh mushrooms

2 tablespoons olive oil

1 small onion, finely chopped

¼ pound mild Italian sausage meat (gluten-free)

¼ cup of gluten-free bread crumbs

¼ teaspoon Italian spice

1 teaspoon salt

1. Preheat oven to 350°F.

2. Carefully remove stems from mushrooms.

3. Chop stems finely and reserve.

4. Place mushroom caps on a cookie sheet covered with greased tin foil.

5. Heat oil in large skillet over moderate heat and cook sausage meat and onion until lightly browned.

6. Add chopped stems to sausage-onion mix and cook for 5 minutes.

7. Add bread crumbs, and Italian seasoning and mix well.

8. Stuff mixture into caps.

9. Bake at 350°F until tender (about 30 minutes). Then broil mushrooms in preheated broiler 3 inches from source of heat for 2–5 minutes.

10. Serve hot.

Spiced Shrimp

SERVES 10–12 (40 pieces)

1 teaspoon paprika

1 teaspoon ground cumin

1 teaspoon brown sugar

½ teaspoon salt

½ teaspoon dry mustard

½ teaspoon oregano

1 pinch each chili and cayenne pepper

1 pound extra-large shrimp (raw)

1 tablespoon extra virgin olive oil

lime wedge (optional)

1. In a small bowl, combine paprika, cumin, sugar, salt, mustard, oregano, chili powder and cayenne.

2. Sprinkle over shrimp in large bowl and toss to coat evenly. Shrimp can be covered and refrigerated for up to 3 hours.

3. In nonstick skillet, heat oil over medium-high heat; stir-fry shrimp until cooked through and no longer opaque, 3 to 4 minutes.

4. Serve hot with lime (if using).

VARIATION
Scallops can also be used. Follow cooking instructions for scallops.

Asparagus Stuffed Chicken with Dijon White Wine Sauce

SERVES 4

4 boneless chicken breasts, pounded flat

2 garlic cloves, crushed

3 tablespoons extra virgin olive oil

1 bunch of asparagus

2¼ cups dry white wine

3 tablespoons Dijon mustard

½ teaspoon sugar

1 tablespoon rice flour

½ teaspoon salt

1. Preheat oven to 375°F.

2. Add 2 tablespoons of oil in a pan over medium heat.

3. Sauté garlic in oil for 2 minutes.

4. Add 2 cups of white wine to pan. Reduce over low heat for 10 minutes.

5. While sauce is reducing, prepare chicken.

6. Pound each chicken breast to ½ inch thick.

7. Place an equal amount of asparagus in each breast. Fold to close and secure with metal skewer.

8. Place in roasting pan and pour remaining oil over top. Sprinkle with salt.

9. Cover and cook at 375°F for 20 minutes. Then cook uncovered for 10 minutes to brown. Internal temperature of chicken should be 165°F.

10. While chicken is cooking, add Dijon mustard and sugar to sauce and stir well.

11. Combine rice flour and ¼ cup of white wine and whisk until blended. Slowly add to sauce while stirring until thickened.

12. Plate chicken, spooning sauce over chicken.

13. Serve with rice (optional).

Prime Rib Roast & Gravy

SERVES 8–10

1 standing rib roast, 3 to 7 ribs
(estimate serving 2–3 people per rib)

salt

freshly ground black pepper

1. Remove the beef roast from the refrigerator 3 hours before cooking. Sprinkle it with salt all over and let it sit.

2. Preheat oven to 500°F (or the highest temp your oven reaches less than 500°F). Pat the roast dry with paper towels and sprinkle the roast all over with salt and pepper.

3. Place the roast fat side up and rib bones down in a roasting pan.

4. Brown the roast at a 500°F temperature in the oven for 15 minutes.

5. Reduce the oven temperature to 325°F. To figure out the total cooking time, allow about 11–12 minutes per pound for rare and 13–15 minutes per pound for medium rare.

   There are so many variables involved that affect cooking time, this is why you should always use a meat thermometer.

   Roast in oven until thermometer registers 115°F for rare or 120°F–130°F for medium (the internal temperature of the roast will continue to rise after you take the roast out of the oven).

   Check the temperature of the roast using a meat thermometer an hour before you expect the roast to be done. If the roast is cooking too quickly at this point, lower the oven temperature to 200°F.

6. Once the roast has reached the temperature you want, remove it from the oven and place it on a carving board. Cover it with foil and let it rest for 30 minutes before carving. The internal temperature of the roast will continue to rise while the roast is resting.

GLUTEN-FREE PRIME RIB GRAVY

3 cups beef broth

1 beef bouillon cube

1–2 tablespoon gluten-free flour mix

salt and pepper

1. To make the gravy, remove the roast from the pan.

2. Place pan on stove on medium high heat.

3. Leaving the drippings in pan, stir in 1 to 2 tablespoons of rice flour or gluten-free flour mix (add more flour if needed).

4. Stir with a wire whisk until the flour has thickened and the gravy is smooth.

5. Heat 1 cup of beef broth and dissolve beef bouillon cube in it.

6. Add the cup of beef broth with the dissolved beef bouillon cube.

7. Continue to add beef broth until gravy is the desired consistency.

8. Continue to cook slowly and stir constantly.

9. Season the gravy with salt and pepper.

10. Serve roast with horseradish.

Cornish Game Hens with Rice Stuffing

SERVES 2

2 (1 pound) cornish game hens

salt and pepper

2 tablespoons slivered almonds (optional)

2 tablespoons onion, finely chopped

⅓ cup uncooked long-grain rice

3 tablespoons mild flavoured extra virgin olive oil

⅔ cup water

1 chicken bouillon cube

1 teaspoon lemon juice

½ teaspoon salt

½ cup sliced sautéed mushrooms

1. Season game hens inside and out with salt and pepper.

2. In small saucepan, cook almonds, onion, and rice in oil for 5 to 10 minutes, stirring frequently.

3. Add water, bouillon cube, lemon juice, and salt.

4. Bring mixture to a boil, stirring to dissolve bouillon cube.

5. Reduce heat; cover and cook slowly about 20–25 minutes or till liquid is absorbed and rice is fluffy. Stir in the sautéed mushrooms.

6. Lightly stuff birds with rice mixture.

7. Place breast side up on the rack in shallow baking pan.

8. Brush with oil.

9. Roast covered at 400°F for 30 minutes.

10. Uncover and roast 1 hour longer or till drumstick can be twisted easily in socket.

11. Brush with oil during last 15 minutes of roasting time.

TIP
Stuffing recipe can be tripled to make a side dish.

Festive Leg of Lamb with Mint Rice Stuffing and Gravy

SERVES 8

3–5 pounds boned leg of lamb

STUFFING

1 onion finely chopped

2 garlic cloves crushed

3 tablespoons extra virgin olive oil

1 package (300g) frozen spinach, chopped

2–3 tablespoons lemon peel, finely grated

1 teaspoon dried mint

½ teaspoon salt and pepper

1½ cups cooked rice

1 (8oz) package of lean cooked chicken or turkey

1. Sauté onion and garlic in oil.

2. Cook spinach in a small amount of water. Cool, squeeze liquid from spinach and chop.

3. Add spinach to onion and garlic along with lemon peel and mint.

4. Add salt and pepper.

5. Add cooked rice.

6. Chop cooked chicken or ham and add to stuffing mixture.

7. Lay out roast and place stuffing in the middle of the boned roast and then tie roast up with string.

8. Place roast meat side down in 325°F oven. Roast uncovered and roast 25 minutes a pound until internal temperature reaches 140°F for medium.

9. Serve with mint sauce and gravy from the drippings.

GLUTEN-FREE LAMB GRAVY

3 cups beef broth

1 beef bouillon cube

1–2 tablespoons gluten-free flour mix

salt and pepper

1. To make the gravy, remove the lamb from the pan.

2. Place pan on stove on medium high heat.

3. Leaving the drippings in pan, stir in 1 to 2 tablespoons of rice flour or gluten-free flour mix (add more flour if needed).

4. Stir with a wire whisk until the flour has thickened and the gravy is smooth.

5. Heat 1 cup of beef broth and dissolve beef bouillon cube in it.

6. Add the cup of beef broth with the dissolved bouillon cube.

7. Continue to add beef broth until gravy is the desired consistency.

8. Continue to cook slowly and stir constantly.

9. Season the gravy with salt and pepper.

Lemon Dill Salmon

SERVES 8

2–3 pounds salmon fillet

4–6 tablespoons extra virgin olive oil

salt and fresh ground black pepper

2 large onions, thinly sliced

2 lemons, cut into slices

2–3 tablespoons fresh dill

1 cup dry white wine, such as Sauvignon Blanc (substitute: chicken broth, or water)

1. Heat oven to 400°F.

2. Place fillet on tinfoil lined baking sheet (salmon fillet will bake wrapped in tinfoil).

3. Pour extra virgin olive oil over salmon.

4. Season both sides of the salmon with salt and pepper.

5. Arrange onion slices first covering salmon fillet then lemon slices on top of onion slices over fillet.

6. Pour wine (or broth) over fillet.

7. Sprinkle fresh dill over fillet.

8. Close tinfoil so fillet cooks in a tinfoil package.

9. Bake the salmon at 400°F for 30 minutes. Checking the temperature of the salmon using an internal thermometer. You want the thickest part of the salmon to read 145°F.

Gluten-Free Apple Crumble (page 234)

DESSERT

Gluten-Free Apple Crumble

SERVES 6–8

5 cups Granny Smith apples, sliced

2 cups gluten-free flour mix

¾ teaspoon xanthan gum (omit if your flour mix already contains it)

½ cup packed light brown sugar

⅓ cup granulated sugar

¼ teaspoon ginger

¼ teaspoon ground cinnamon

¼ teaspoon nutmeg

⅓ cup dairy-free margarine

¼ cup chopped nuts (optional)

dairy-free whipping cream or dairy-free ice cream (optional)

1. Preheat oven to 375°F.

2. Place apple slices in greased 8-inch by 8-inch square baking dish. Stir in the granulated sugar.

3. To prepare the crumble topping. In a medium-sized bowl, place the flour, xanthan gum, brown sugar, cinnamon, nutmeg and ginger.

4. Cut in margarine until the mixture resembles coarse crumble.

5. Stir in nuts if using.

6. Sprinkle crumble over fruit.

7. Bake in 375°F oven for 30–35 minutes or until fruit is tender and topping is golden.

8. If desired, serve warm with dairy-free vanilla ice cream or coconut whipping cream.

Fruit Cocktail in Pineapple Shells

SERVES 6–8

1 large fresh pineapple

5 seedless mandarin oranges, peeled and sectioned (reserve juice)

3 kiwifruits, peeled and cubed

3 cups whole strawberries, washed, hulled and cut in halves or quarters

1 cup each green, purple and red grapes, washed and left whole

1. Cut pineapple in half lengthwise right through stalk.

2. In a large bowl, add all the fruit.

3. Scoop pineapple out, adding juice and pineapple to bowl, discarding core. Mix all fruit well.

4. Arrange pineapple halves on serving plate, top and tail fashion. Put as much fruit into shells as they will take.

5. Serve remaining fruit and juice in a serving bowl.

6. If making in advance, leave the fruit salad in a bowl in the refrigerator until required. Put fruit into pineapple shells when ready to serve.

Peach Almond Delight

SERVES 2

3 fresh peaches

4 oz slivered almonds

2 tablespoons dates, diced

1 teaspoon cinnamon

½ teaspoon natural vanilla extract

½ cup water

1. Wash the peaches and cut each into eight sections.

2. Mix with the almonds and dates.

3. Drizzle with vanilla and sprinkle cinnamon on top.

Paleo Pumpkin Squares

MAKES 16–20

1 cup canned pumpkin puree

⅓ cup pure maple syrup (or honey)

4 large eggs

2 cups almond flour

¼ teaspoon sea salt

1 teaspoon baking soda

½ teaspoon ground cinnamon

½ teaspoon ground nutmeg

½ teaspoon ground cloves

1. Preheat oven to 350°F.

2. In a food processor combine pumpkin, maple syrup, and eggs. Blend for 2 minutes.

3. Blend dry ingredients into wet ingredients until well blended.

4. Pour batter into a 8 x 11 baking dish greased with oil.

5. Bake for 35–40 minutes.

6. Let cool for 15 minutes.

7. Cut into squares.

Banana Chocolate Chip Muffins

MAKES 12

2 cups gluten-free baking flour

1½ teaspoons gluten-free baking soda

1 teaspoon gluten-free baking powder

1 teaspoon xanthan gum

⅓ cup canola oil

1 egg (or replacer)

⅔ cup coconut milk (or other alternative)

1 teaspoon vinegar

3 ripe bananas

½ cup honey

½ cup apple sauce

1 teaspoon vanilla extract

1 cup dairy-free chocolate chips and/or nuts (optional)

1. Preheat oven to 350°F.

2. Mix flour, baking soda, baking powder, xanthan gum ingredients in medium size bowl.

3. Mix coconut milk (or other milk alternative i.e. almond or rice milk) and vinegar in separate bowl and set aside.

4. Mash bananas until almost smooth and set aside.

5. In a large bowl, beat oil and egg together.

6. Mix in honey, apple sauce and vanilla.

7. Add mashed bananas and milk mixture and stir well.

8. Add half the dry mixture to wet ingredients and stir well.

9. Stir in remaining dry mixture.

10. Add in dairy-free chocolate chips and/or nuts if desired.

11. Line muffin tin with baking cups and fill each ⅔ full with batter. Should make 12 large or 24 mini muffins.

12. Bake at 350°F for 17–20 minutes. Tops should be light brown.

Berry Citrus Horizon

SERVES 3

1 cup fresh strawberries

1 cup fresh blueberries

½ tangerine, sectioned

1 tablespoon orange juice

1 teaspoon natural vanilla extract

ground nutmeg

fresh mint for garnish

1. Mix the strawberries, blueberries, and tangerine sections in a bowl.

2. Add orange juice and vanilla and stir.

3. Sprinkle with nutmeg.

4. Serve chilled and garnished with mint.

Cantaloupe Stuffed with Blackberries & Pecans

SERVES 4

1 cantaloupe

1 cup blackberries

½ cup pecans, chopped

mint leaves for garnish

1. Cut cantaloupe in half and scoop out seeds.

2. Quarter cantaloupe.

3. Fill each cavity with berries and pecans.

4. Garnish with mint leaves.

Gluten-Free Soft Pretzels

SERVES 12

1 cup cassava flour

1 cup almond flour

4 eggs

3 tablespoons avocado oil (or coconut oil)

2 tablespoons maple syrup

2 tablespoons apple cider vinegar

1 teaspoon sea salt

1 teaspoon baking powder

1 egg (for egg wash)

salt to taste (for topping)

1. Preheat oven to 400°F.

2. Line a baking sheet with parchment paper.

3. Combine all the ingredients for the dough in an electric mixer, (if you're mixing by hand ensure the dough is well mixed).

4. Bring a medium saucepan of water to a boil. Keep water at a boil.

5. Break off pieces of the dough and roll into to 1-inch thick rolls. Fold rolls into a pretzel shape, or a ring.

6. Drop the first pretzel into the boiling water, and let it cook for 1 minute.

7. Remove the pretzel from the water with a handheld strainer.

8. Place the pretzel on the baking sheet. Continue until all the pretzels have been boiled and are on the baking sheet.

9. Brush the pretzels with the egg wash and sprinkle to taste with coarse salt.

10. Bake at 400°F for around 20 minutes, or until golden and crisp.

Store-bought Gluten and Dairy Free Desserts:
Apple Pie, Pumpkin Pie, Espresso Cheesecake,
Berry Cheesecake, Chocolate Cake

Dairy-Free and Gluten-Free Desserts Available in Stores

When we started following this diet over 24 years ago, there was a very limited selection of gluten, dairy and soy free products, especially desserts. Fortunately that is no longer the case and there are a number of delicious Best Bet Diet friendly desserts that you can easily find in the frozen section of most grocery or health food stores.

Be sure to read the labels to ensure they do not contain gluten, dairy, soy, pea protein, peanuts or any of the other foods to exclude listed on pages 38–42.

Conclusion

Recommended Reading

There are many books that we have found helpful and inspiring over the years. Here is a list of books we recommend if you would like more information on Multiple Sclerosis and Nutrition:

Managing Multiple Sclerosis Naturally
A Self-Help Guide to Living with MS
by Judy Graham (2012)

The Multiple Sclerosis Diet Book
A Low-Fat Diet for the Treatment of MS., Revised and Expanded Edition
by Dr. Roy Laver Swank and Barbara Brewer Dugan (1987)

Roger MacDougall Story
http://www.direct-ms.org/resources/testimonials/roger-mcdougall-story

The Paleo Diet
Lose Weight and Get Healthy by Eating the Food You Were Designed to Eat
by Dr. Loren Cordain (2010)

Overcoming Multiple Sclerosis
An Evidence-based Guide to Recovery
by Dr George Jelinek (2012)

Recovering from Multiple Sclerosis
Real Life Stories of Hope and Inspiration
by Dr. George Jelinek and Karen Law (2013)

The Wahls Protocol
How I Beat Progressive MS Using Paleo Principles and Functional Medicine
by Dr. Terry Wahls with Eve Adamson (2014)

FINAL THOUGHTS

I hope that you have found this cookbook useful. When Mathew received the diagnosis of MS, it was a difficult time for our entire family. Within days of the diagnosis, we received Judy Graham's and Dr. Swank's books from friends, and their books gave us hope.

As you know, Ashton did the research that led to the creation of the Best Bet Diet. As a family with three teenage sons, the implementation of the diet wasn't easy, but our family came together as a unit and accepted these dietary changes.

It will take time to make the necessary changes to adapt to the Best Bet Diet but, once you have, it will become second nature. In our experience, it took about six months to feel comfortable with the diet and to find stores with the appropriate products.

I wrote this book in the hope that it would be helpful to other families who are dealing with MS and choose to embrace these dietary strategies. It can be very overwhelming at the start, but it has been well worth it for us.

I wish you well and please feel free to contact us at info@direct-ms.org. We are happy to answer questions and would enjoy hearing your comments and suggestions.

Tribute to Joan Embry (1949–2020)

Joan Margaret Embry loving wife, mother, grandmother, sister, volunteer, friend, nurse extraordinaire and the creator and compiler of the Best Bet Cookbook, died peacefully at home on April 1, 2020.

Joan's primary focus was always her family, and she raised her three adventurous sons, Mat, Dean and Duncan with compassion and caring. Over the past eleven years she had the joy of the arrival of four grandchildren whom she adored and looked after at every opportunity. Sleepovers at Grandma's house were always filled with fun and great meals.

Nursing was in Joan's blood and she enjoyed thirty years of community nursing with a focus on the care of seniors. One of the projects she spearheaded was the Northwest Seniors Network which helped seniors live independently in their communities for as long as possible by providing increased community support. She also established the Seniors' Christmas Dinner which was held on Christmas Day for senior citizens living alone.

For the past 25 years Joan also made important contributions to helping persons with multiple sclerosis (MS) all over the world. When her son Mathew received the devastating diagnosis of MS in 1995, Joan immediately went into action-mode and she and Ashton devised a science-based nutrition program to counter the effects of MS. This nutritional therapy has kept Mathew in great health for the last 25 years.

Motivated to take their MS research to the world, Joan was the driving force for creating and setting up a federally registered charity, Direct-MS, in 1996 to provide science-based information on the use of nutritional strategies for combatting MS and to fund research on nutrition for multiple sclerosis. Tens of thousands of persons with MS have used this information to successfully keep MS well controlled.

Her final contribution to the MS community was the recent publication of this volume which provides many tips for implementing the Best Bet Diet for MS as well as 125 recipes. Joan's work in MS had an international impact and, when her passing was announced on social media, thousands of people from all over the world reached out to express their love for her and how she touched their lives.

RECIPE INDEX

VEGETABLES CONT.

INSTANT POT

SLOW COOKING

DESSERT